# HOW TO TURN YOUR HOLIDAYS INTO POPULAR FICTION

# HOW TO TURN YOUR HOLIDAYS INTO POPULAR FICTION

*Kate Nivison*

ALLISON & BUSBY

First published in Great Britain in 1994 by
Allison & Busby
an imprint of Wilson & Day Ltd
5 The Lodge
Richmond Way
London W12 8LW

A catalogue record for this book is available from the British Library

ISBN 0 7490 0113 5

Typeset by TW Typesetting, Plymouth, Devon
Printed and bound in Great Britain by
Mackays of Chatham Ltd, Chatham, Kent

# CONTENTS

# INTRODUCTION:
# THE WORLD IS YOUR STAGE

Every story has to take place somewhere, and *somewhere* is a very big place. This book is to help you, the fiction writer, to get the most out of that *somewhere*, whatever your genre – family sagas, romance, blockbusters, mystery, horror or crime.

For some writers, there is a particular place where they are 'at home' – a place they know and love so well that it is the main source of their inspiration. Daphne du Maurier (Cornwall) and Catherine Cookson (North-East England) are just two of the many hugely successful writers in this category.

But other writers are not so deeply rooted, and maybe you are one of these. After all, in the world of the imagination there are no boundaries. Quite literally, the whole world is your stage and the sheer range of choices can be frightening. But like all good frights, it can also be stimulating.

So this is not a book for those who want to stay at home. It is for anyone who wants to write fiction who likes to 'venture abroad' in any sense of the term.

Abroad is a wonderful place. It starts anywhere that you don't consider home and goes on to the most exotic locations imaginable. For most of us, it means holidays, while others will have been born or worked abroad. Using such backgrounds is a way of challenging yourself and your readers. You are bringing them something outside their usual experience, and that in itself can affect the creative process in a surprising number of ways.

While marketing is not within the scope of this book, one glance at the titles in the nearest library or book shop, or indeed at the film and video listings, will convince you that exotic locations are as popular as ever. But be in no doubt – even readers who have never been abroad have some degree of familiarity with an enormous variety of places through television and cinema. It is not so much that locations have to be increasingly outlandish, although something set in Patagonia, Sarawak or Nagorno-Karabakh might indeed make a welcome change. It is simply that readers today both deserve and expect something more than the same old purple sunsets, atmospheric ruins, waving palms, snow-capped mountains and sapphire seas.

You will, of course, be following in a long tradition, starting with Shakespeare, who set almost all his comedies and tragedies outside England. Many of our most distinguished novelists have done the same – Joseph Conrad, E. M. Forster, Graham Greene, Evelyn Waugh, Christopher Isherwood, Paul Scott, Anthony Burgess and numerous others. Today we have Ian McEwan and William Boyd, and you probably have your own favourites. With writers of this calibre, you can be sure that their choice of a foreign location was not just a matter of pure escapism or exoticism for the sake of it.

Don't be intimidated by the credentials of star turns such as these. Writers are always advised to write about what they know, and I hope this book will show you that what you know is often a whole lot more than you think. Careful preparation and research, brushing up your observation and recording technique, making maximum use of the available technology – all can work wonders for your confidence when it comes to tackling an exotic setting. The same techniques should also be helpful if your chosen setting is no further than your own back yard.

So if you have travelled at all, or are already planning your next package tour, polar expedition, fly-drive, walking holiday or day trip, why not make sure that you really get your money's worth out of it? Think of yourself as being not just on holiday, but *on location*. You'll get so much more out of your trip if you are well prepared, and your knowledge will come through to the readers. They'll find themselves transported along with you – and that is surely the purpose of all good fiction.

# 1

# WHY AN EXOTIC BACKGROUND?

If you are writing fiction to sell, the very best reason for setting your work abroad is that the readers like it. Those magic words 'set against a gorgeous backdrop' have instant shelf appeal. But perhaps you are not quite ready yet to consider the marketing side of things. Perhaps you feel your writing is in a rut, or you would like to make use of some particularly interesting travel or holiday experiences in your fiction. Wherever you are in your writing career, it's well worth taking a fresh look at the basics of fiction in this context to see how the use of an exotic setting can enhance your work.

## Back to basics

For any work of fiction, whether it is a short story, serial, novel, drama or screenplay, the basics are more or less the same – plot or storyline, theme, structure, characters, atmosphere, style and pace. The order used here may not necessarily reflect the relative importance of each for your particular genre. Some writers instinctively put *theme* first, and let their storyline develop from that. For others, the *characters* have to come alive first before they can find either a theme or a plot. But whatever your genre – or method – choosing a foreign location can have some fascinating and useful spin-offs.

## Hatching the plot

The plot or storyline is the action that moves your work forward. It is about happenings, incidents, one thing leading to another. It has to involve an *adventure*, whether on the physical, spiritual, intellectual or emotional plane. This adventure can be on any scale, from an old lady finally getting round to posting a letter to the daughter she hasn't seen for years to a shoot-out over several continents.

But adventures don't usually happen 'at home'. Indeed, almost by definition, home is where adventures *don't* happen. Home is where you are safe, where life is as predictable as it's ever likely to be, where people understand you, and where you know the rules. That's not to say that nothing ever happens 'at home' that could make good fiction. Any kind of change or intrusion can trigger a good story of any length, from new neighbours, pregnancy, divorce or old age, to accidents, break-ins, blocked drains or a plague of rats. So far, you may have been content to venture no further. After all, Alan Bennett has built his whole career on the minutiae of home, while at the other end of the domestic respectability range is Julie Burchill, one of the most highly paid writers around, who maintains that she has never set foot outside the country.

The possibilities for developing a good plot increase enormously, however, when you venture *abroad*. Let's take that in its generally accepted sense these days to mean leaving the country, at least as far as the plot is concerned.

The most obvious point is that abroad can be dangerous in ways we've almost forgotten about in the British Isles (excluding Northern Ireland and the odd terrorist bomb) and danger is good for the plot. In far too many countries, even those with a thriving or once thriving tourist industry, there are civil disturbances, local wars, security restrictions, political violence overt or covert, dreadful social injustices and all the problems associated with them. The Balkans, Egypt and Israel are obvious recent examples, and further afield the list is endless. Sometimes it is possible to visit one country as a tourist, while just over the border in almost identical terrain, mayhem is raging. You can now visit Albania on a day trip from Corfu, see Cambodia or Burma from comparatively peaceful Thailand, and witness appalling social contrasts in many large cities from an air-conditioned coach. Even in the United States, urban areas of considerable danger are in close proximity to regular tourist beats.

Try making a list of countries you consider safe, starting with Belgium, and you will find it amazingly short. That may be regrettable, but it makes the rest potentially *exciting*. As some countries come off the list for certain types of plots, others come on. Where could Graham Greene have set *The Third Man* but in post-war Vienna, and what will all the spy writers do without Berlin's notorious Checkpoint Charlie? But a writer visiting Vienna or Berlin today would quickly find some other kind of story waiting to be told. Meanwhile, other countries, other cities, are earning their place on the danger list, providing a fertile breeding ground for any number of stories from the heart-rending to the life-threatening.

The way you use these places to hatch your plot, or simply thicken it, depends on a basic choice you have to make for your main protagonists about their degree of involvement in local affairs. Your protagonists could be:

- actively involved in what is going on, for whatever motive;
- unwittingly involved at first, but becoming caught up, eagerly or reluctantly;
- following a quite different agenda, which is then heavily influenced by the events around them.

The first option, active involvement, often requires specialised local knowledge, and the end result may well be something in the thriller category, especially if the setting is contemporary. However, writers of romance and family sagas often set this kind of personal entanglement in exciting/ dangerous local events, particularly if they deal with the

3

colonial past (India or Africa) or immigrant themes (Australia, Canada, USA). This is because their main characters tend to be native English speakers. Making them anything else can be very difficult to get right unless you have specialised knowledge of, say, East European/Jewish farmers in the last century, Chinese peasant life, medieval Italian nobles and so on, or come from the area yourself.

If you are a beginner, it is far easier to tackle the other two, where the degree of involvement in local affairs is less, but can still be used to help the plot along. Since the protagonist is likely to be abroad for some professional reason, even a minimal knowledge of some topic or occupation can go a long way when transplanted somewhere else. Don't feel that just because your setting is exotic, your protagonist's line of work has to reek of glamour too. They can't all be fashion designers, spies, art historians, journalists or sky-divers. There is a huge range of occupations and interests apart from the more obvious ones of police work, high finance or the travel business itself that could be 'sent on holiday' to somewhere different, romantic or downright dangerous. If you have expertise in any of the following or can add to the list from your own experience, why not go for an occupation-centred plot based somewhere other than your own back yard?

- Politics – local or national;
- Education and training – primary, secondary, or higher;
- Medicine or community/social work;
- Farming, animal welfare or horticulture;
- Running a shop, restaurant, garage or other small business;
- Playing an instrument, singing or dancing.

Go for the unconventional here – anything rather than the traditional nanny/secretary syndrome.

For long fiction it might be useful to consider *varying the degree of local involvement* among your characters, so that one might be totally committed to the local scene, another gets caught up in it, while a third sees himself as just passing through and behaves like an ostrich throughout. The tension between the characters' different degrees of local involvement could also form an important element of the plot. There is more about the emotional effects of location on your characters under the relevant heading later in this chapter.

Your main protagonist might simply be a tourist, of course, and tourists do have adventures, romantic or otherwise, which provide a rich source of plots of the kind probably best suited to short stories.

In addition to the location-inspired plot – a story which could only happen because of the circumstances in that particular place – it is perfectly possible to take any situation that could happen at home and transplant it to somewhere exotic. There is always the danger, however, that in unskilled hands that's how it will read. Editors call this the 'It happened in Marrakesh, but it might as well have been Margate' syndrome. Above all, bear in mind that, while most of us only have experience of abroad as tourists or short-term visitors, you as a writer certainly need not confine your characters in that way if you do your homework thoroughly. See Chapter 2.

## Developing a theme

Not all popular fiction has a theme as such, nor even requires one, but most fiction is deepened and enriched by a theme, such as ambition, sibling rivalry, betrayal, conflicting loyalties, greed, obsession, the fleeting nature of happiness, love or life, or whatever.

A theme doesn't have to be concerned with emotions, but can be something very down to earth, like 'crime doesn't (or does) pay', 'rags to riches', corruption in high places, or the effects of tourism on a local community.

However, if you experiment with some of the above (in any case only a very small sample of available themes) by applying them to another culture, new possibilities immediately open up. How much more dramatic sibling rivalry can become in a culture where the oldest son inherits all. Where does nepotism (endemic in some cultures) end and corruption begin, and can your hero/heroine understand the difference? In some countries, aggressive upward mobility is understood and appreciated, whether the protagonist is male or female. In others, even a virtuous Cinderella would have a hard time if she tried to climb the social ladder, whether she belongs to that culture or not. As an outsider, her struggles to be accepted, let alone successful, would be even greater, as in Oswald Wynd's delightful *The Ginger Tree*, set in Japan.

Placing your story in a country foreign to your main character will also automatically expand your range of possible themes to include the theme of tension between cultures. In fact, some of the most successful books set entirely outside Britain such as E. M. Forster's *A Passage to India*, have this 'n'er the twain shall meet' theme. There have been brilliant attempts to bridge the gap or explore it, like T. E. Lawrence's *Seven Pillars of Wisdom* and Paul Scott's *Raj Quartet*. Evelyn Waugh does it with humour in *Black Mischief* as do both William Boyd (*A Good Man in Africa*) and Tom Sharpe (*Riotous Assembly*).

Karen Blixen's *Out of Africa* is supposed to be autobiography rather than fiction, but her book is a reinterpretation of her own life where the theme of 'loss of Eden' is so strong that any fiction writer can learn from it.

Other possibilities include the need to escape (from what and why) and the dread and uncertainty of returning home (Paul Scott's *Staying On*). The sense of impermanence, of up-rootedness, of living on borrowed time, the search for one's roots – all these can make valuable and fascinating additions to the more usual repertoire of home-based themes.


## Shaping the structure

A foreign location can be a great advantage when it comes to providing a framework in time and space within which the story can happen. Some writers hate the very idea of imposing such limits on their work, especially in the initial stages, but many others will recognise a far more common problem – that of tying the story down before it spins out of control and flies off all over the place. Agatha Christie knew what she was doing by getting everyone together in a large country house, preferably surrounded by misty marshes. That way, useful limits can be imposed and the writer is more in control. It is becoming increasingly difficult to find convincing and original 'sealed environments' or focal points in our own society, but simply by setting your story abroad, you can increase your chances of finding one. The simple fact is that most expatriates abroad still tend to congregate in certain places – Rick's Bar in *Casablanca* being perhaps the best known example of one type of closed setting. The original title was actually *Everybody Comes to Rick's*. In times of crisis, they'll congregate even more.

If your protagonists are visiting or working abroad, however temporarily, they will undoubtedly get sucked into one of these focal points, whether they like it or not. And don't feel restricted to the bar or club. There are so many more to choose from.

You will certainly be able to add to this list of possibilities:

| | |
|---|---|
| college campus | oil rig |
| lonely research station | secret guerilla base |
| refugee camp | hospital |
| civil lines (British India) | amateur dramatic society |
| mission | diplomatic/foreign sector of |
| holiday camp | town |
| cruise liner | specialist touring holiday |
| time-share 'village' | large hotel complex |
| camp site | aid workers' headquarters |
| company headquarters | |

Making use of such focal points has the huge advantage of keeping your protagonists quite naturally at very close quarters, which in itself can lead to all sorts of interesting situations. Such 'sealed units' can also be used to force your characters apart when necessary. Think of all those high walls, locked gates and security guards, while within are the more subtle barriers of race, status and class which we still somehow manage to bring with us even while trying to get away from it all.

Then there is the question of a *time* structure and here 'abroad' can be invaluable. Far more than at home, activities have time limits. A holiday, by definition, has to come to an end, leave is at prearranged times, contracts expire, fresh personnel arrive, the rains start, the tourist season finishes and so on. The beauty of all this is that you are in control of the timetable, and there is nothing like having a deadline to make something happen. Naturally you won't forget to exploit the intensity of relationships that tend to develop in these circumstances, where the sense of a time limit imposes a kind of urgency not generally found at home unless there is a war on.

Another useful structural device is the *quest*, search or hunt of some sort. That way there is a progression, however fraught, towards a clear goal, and a natural conclusion when the search is rewarded. The search might be for anything – buried treasure, lost friends or relatives, criminals, antiques, even one's own roots. While it is perfectly feasible to base a story round this kind of thing on your home patch, setting it abroad multiplies the possibilities and makes the whole thing potentially more unpredictable and exciting.

Now is the time to exploit the 'Things Fall Apart' syndrome, regrettably so common to many of those far away places with the strange-sounding names. One of Nigeria's finest writers, Chinua Achebe, did exactly that in his ground-breaking novel of that name, taken from W. B. Yeats's 'Things fall apart/The centre cannot hold . . .' Indeed there are many places where general breakdown is a way of life – even an art form. The effects can be funny, sad, disastrous, challenging, whatever you want them to be. John Mortimer built most of *Summer's Lease* around the vicissitudes of the water supply to a villa in Tuscany (or more cruelly, Chiantishire). But if you want a masterclass in turning picturesque chaos into sound literary structure and don't mind a little political incorrectness, try Evelyn Waugh's *Black Mischief*.

## Challenging your characters

For any work of fiction to succeed, the characters have to evolve or change in some way. Of course they can do this perfectly well at home, given the right circumstances, but by sending your characters abroad, you are automatically setting them up for a change, for a challenge. Try making a list of changes that are supposed to take place in people (particularly the British) when they go abroad. It might begin something like this:

- The young men get drunk and aggressive;
- The girls get swept off their feet at the first hint of romance;
- Senior citizens can't cope with the food;
- We expect to be understood even if we don't speak a word of the local language;
- We get defensive if Britain is criticised, embarrassed by beggars, furious at the way animals are treated, confused by the currency, paranoid about being ripped off and generally behave as if the normal rules of safety and good manners don't apply.

Stereotyping? Possibly – but the rumours have got round somehow.

When people do behave like this, it's worth thinking hard about why, because unless you are into anti-heroes/heroines, your characters are *not* going to behave like that. Why not? Is it their education and background, natural friendliness and curiosity, inhibitions, an innate sense of self-preservation? Could it be a strong need to be invisible, to lose themselves in another culture, a flair for languages or a thirst for

9

something different? Would one of your characters at first sight appear to fit a stereotype, and then break out of the mould?

Of course there are always characters such as P. G. Wodehouse's unflappable Jeeves, whose chief strength is in remaining unchanged whatever the surroundings. But most people react quite strongly to being abroad and therefore act differently. Look at these contrasting reactions:

| Positive | Negative |
|---|---|
| Excited | Tense, apprehensive |
| Stimulated | Bored |
| Bowled over, enchanted | Disgusted, shocked |
| Fitter, healthier | Languid, ill |
| Welcomed, involved | Homesick, alienated |
| Genuinely interested | Sensation-seeking |
| Relaxed | Infuriated, scared |

Don't be content with responses to strange food, climate, creepy-crawlies or social customs. Your character might be quite unphased by these, but be knocked off balance by something apparently minor – unfamiliar night noises, an enforced siesta time, lack of TV, or having extra leisure because of domestic help or living in a hotel. How do they react to being higher up the social scale simply because they are white, privileged or rich compared with the local people? Or are they further down it – as a servant to the rich, a 'foreign devil', or simply by being a woman? Does your hero or heroine feel comfortable in his/her own skin? How do they react to being 'shown the ropes' by real or self-appointed experts?

Think carefully about which parts of the world might suit, or definitely not suit, the character you have in mind. If you have a part of the world you want to use, think of the kind of character who would blossom (or shrivel up) in that place. How would a heroine who is adopted react to being thrust into a warm, noisy Italian family environment where blood ties are everything? How would the highly independent young wife of an older diplomat cope with the restrictions of a Middle Eastern posting?

10

One old trick for discovering extra dimensions or hidden layers to your characters is to try seeing them through someone else's eyes. My 'other eyes' are those of a wise old expatriate I knew who reckoned that if anyone had a serious personality flaw, a short spell in Africa would find it. He claimed he could tell in one evening whether someone was FPH material (First Plane Home) or hooked for life – and he was almost never wrong. Ask yourself what he might have been looking for, then try it on your characters.

## Creating that atmosphere

By its very nature, atmosphere is difficult stuff to pin down and analyse. This is because our feelings are involved as well as our powers of observation and physical sensitivity. What we perceive as the atmosphere of a place comes to us by a two-way exchange. You can say that a place makes you feel something, but very often what you feel is strongly influenced by what you brought along in the shape of your own emotional luggage (expectations, state of mind, memories). Sometimes what we bring with us is simply a stereotyped view of what the atmosphere of a place should be.

When it comes to atmosphere, the task of the fiction writer is rather different from that of a writer of travel features. A travel writer will try to capture as faithfully as possible the atmosphere of a place – to record it, to encapsulate it, in an interesting and original way. There will, of course, be some degree of selection involved, depending on whether the travel article is purely informative or a mood piece.

For the fiction writer, however, the main priority is to *create* an atmosphere that is suitable for the story being told, and this involves a far greater degree of selection. Neither kind of writing should take liberties with the facts, but there is a huge difference in emphasis here.

This is not to say that you can't write a story where a place's atmosphere dominates or even dictates the plot. It is hard to detach, say, Bram Stoker's *Dracula* from that storm-lit castle in the dark Transylvanian woods – but approaching it the other way round can be very liberating. If you have a good story to tell, make sure you choose a place whose atmosphere complements or enhances the story rather than slows it down or swamps it. Atmospheric detail should always relate to some facet of the story, and the more subtly you do this the better. (For more about matching atmospheric detail to mood, see Chapter 9.)

Now I am not suggesting here that you neglect your basic homework on what you personally feel gives a place atmosphere. In fact subsequent chapters deal with recording as much of this atmosphere as you can, as accurately as possible. What I do suggest at this point, is accepting two things:

1. What you *observe* will have already gone through your own subconscious 'emotional vetting' process. You may therefore be missing something and could need to look at things more widely and more deeply.

2. You will have to be *consciously and heavily selective* in what you *use* from your observations.

Of course travel feature writers know this too. Some of the best travel writing is very focused, and focus implies selection, both subconscious and deliberate. But as fiction writers we too should always be aware that it is the kind of story we wish to write that must influence our final selection of those important atmospheric details.

Try this exercise. Take a couple of places thought to reek of atmosphere – an Arab *souk* and a Greek fishing village. Now go along with all the atmospheric clichés that spring to mind.

**Arab *souk*** or covered bazaar – mysterious, dark, shady in both senses of the word, even threatening: not too clean, full of strange smells, jostling, alive with argument and barter, poor, male dominated. Colours: buff, sand, or strong to vibrant.

**Greek fishing village** – sunny and bright, open, public, liberating, sense of community, continuity, simplicity, honest toil. Colours: blue, white, red/pink geraniums.

Dismiss these examples as unimaginative stereotyping if

you like, but the 'accepted' atmosphere more or less suggests the sort of stories that might be set in both these locations as here described. But suppose a thriller writer is on holiday in a Greek village, or a romantic novelist visits a North African *souk*. You could finish up with something like this:

**Arab** *souk* – welcoming to lovers for its warmth, shadows and intimacy; erotic with strange perfumes, veiled bodies and a hint of the forbidden; knowing glances from the women. Even the very intensity of the sunlight between the shadows ... and so on. It certainly worked for Rudolf Valentino. Would it work for you?

**Greek fishing village** – now we have the shadows after the glare. What are those men playing backgammon really talking about? Why are there so many widows, and anyway, where are all the women today? Do the cats have to be so painfully thin? And those blood-red geraniums spilling down the walls ...

For each of the places listed below, jot down what you think of as its traditional atmosphere. Even if you haven't been there, the guide books and travel programmes may have done it for you:

| | |
|---|---|
| Alpine village | French camp site |
| Italian town square | Desert oasis |
| Tropical lagoon | Spanish villa |

Then think again, turning it all round as above. It isn't a new trick, of course – not when we remember that it was an Alpine village which gave us not only *Heidi* and *The Sound of Music*, but one of the great horror classics – Mary Shelley's *Frankenstein*. Bob Dylan in 'She Belongs to Me' sings of a woman who could 'take the dark out of the night time and paint the day time black'. Perhaps she was a fiction writer.

**Quickening the pace**

Some editors insist that pace is everything these days, and the

Queen of the Breathlessness has to be Judith Krantz. For sheer verve (or is it nerve?) her opening scene in *I'll Take Manhattan* is hard to beat. She has her New York-bound heroine, Maxi Amberville, giving the poor stewardess a hard time simply because she's so impatient to get off the plane. Fair enough, with a name like that what would you expect? But the girl is on Concorde, for goodness' sake, and they don't come much pacier than that unless you have your own space shuttle.

It is certainly true that pace has a great deal to do with the way you write rather than the actual content. But it has to be said that sending your characters on a journey can do much to generate that vital sense of anticipation in your readers.

With a story set abroad, there is the obvious ploy of starting with the journey there, but it's been done so many times before, and not just by Ms Krantz's impatient heroine. These days few people do anything else but arrive by plane, so unless you can think of a good twist on all the variations of taking off, flying, landing, or being met, it's probably better to get off to a flying start (please excuse the pun/cliché) some other way.

Thanks to a chance remark by a friend, I found a new twist for the opening of a serial set in Thailand (*The Hills of Heaven*, *Woman's Weekly*). Our heroine is already in the country on a forestry research station, and is at Chiang Mai airport with her husband to meet the new troubleshooter. The Bangkok plane is delayed, and as she stares in boredom at the monsoon rain, a little four-seater hurtles out of the clouds and out steps the man who will almost wreck her marriage. He's hitched a lift on an American mission plane. That's what my friend had done when visiting up-country New Guinea. I was impressed – and so was our heroine.

On more classical lines when it comes to pace setting, it is worth noting that, in spite of its title, *A Passage to India* doesn't deal with 'getting there' at all. Instead it starts with a leisurely description of the town of Chandrapore. Then, in a masterly change of pace, Forster suddenly gives us this:

Abandoning his bicycle, which fell before a servant could catch it, the young man sprang up onto the veranda. He was all animation. 'Hamidullah, Hamidullah! Am I late?' he cried.

Note what Forster achieves in this tiny paragraph:

- the idea that the young man is probably Indian rather than European, and that Indians have servants too;
- his energy, his anxiety;
- the image of the bicycle and veranda, so typical of India;
- the knowledge that something important is about to happen.

Then there is the sheer speed of the action. Later Forster gives us fraught journeys by horse-drawn tongas, the fateful elephant trip to the Malabar Caves and the final horse ride that only serves to widen the space between Fielding and Aziz. Each has its own pace perfectly tuned to the subject matter.

*A Passage to India* also reminds us of the huge amount of time people outside our small islands spend travelling. Returning holidaymakers constantly remark how big even places like France, Spain and Turkey are compared with Britain. Your characters need not go in for continent-hopping on the Krantz scale, but there's nothing like a journey to lend impetus to the plot. The movement can also act as a foil to what might otherwise be static heart searching. In other words, get them moving while they are recapping, pondering their next step or regretting their last. For getting the most out of journeys, see Chapter 3.

## Enhancing your style

Style is usually defined as the writer's individual voice; the way he or she puts words together. Some experts say that the hallmark of good style is clarity, at which we have to ask where this leaves writers like Marcel Proust and James Joyce. Some maintain that style can be taught, others that it can only be refined, corrected or channelled, and then only to a very minor degree.

Leaving these controversial aspects aside however, it is worth asking why so many of our best and most commercially successful writers whose mother tongue is English were either born abroad, or have lived abroad for long periods. Some are nationals of other English-speaking countries. You will be able to add to those already mentioned, and it is certainly worth glancing at the prize-winner lists for the more prestigious fiction competitions – the Booker Prize, for example, won in 1993 by Irish writer Roddy Doyle. Then there are the Ian St James Awards, Bridport Arts, and Stand Magazine competitions. In most years, up to half the winners are from Ireland, Northern Ireland, Scotland, North America or elsewhere, while the biographies or the story contents of others often reveal an extensive knowledge of life and work abroad.

What I am suggesting here is that such writers may have an edge on the rest of us which they have exploited to the full, and that this edge could be as much to do with the *style* of their writing as in the actual setting or the content of their work. In *The Story of English*, authors McCrum, Cran and MacNeil note the rise of many types of English all over the world, from Cockney, Scouse, Scots and Geordie, to Creole, Pidgeon, Strine, Singlish, Franglais and so on.

What I am *not* suggesting is that you plunge whole-heartedly into dialect – far from it, unless your work is essentially folkloric in character. Many readers find wodges of dialect very off-putting, however colourful – and so do editors. But when you choose an exotic background for your work, the chances are that at least some of the characters will be local people, and it is well worth trying to develop an ear for the way they express themselves. Even long-term expatriates in distant places soon develop speech patterns and expressions that are very different from the way they would speak at home. To the newcomer it can sound like a code, which can be irritating – but it can also be funny, inventive, effective and evocative. Read some work by writers living in a place that interests you, and almost subconsciously you will pick up the flavour of something different that will seep into your work.

This has to be very subtle. To use a simple analogy – a friend of mine professes to hate garlic, yet his wife has been adding touches of it to his food for years. He hasn't noticed it, but often complains that other food lacks flavour. For an example of this subtlety, look again at the piece from *A Passage to India* quoted earlier. How do we guess that the young man springing so precipitously from his bicycle is Indian? Perhaps it is just the thought that an Englishman in the British Raj would be more on his dignity or be feeling the heat too much to rush about like that. But the real giveaway is that staccato repetition of his friend's name and the abruptness of the question. This man is not an Edwardian Englishman.

If you are a beginner writer whose mother tongue is not English, or you are from an area with a strong regional English of its own, like the Caribbean, various parts of Africa and the Far East, I would suggest that you keep your own 'voice' as far as possible. By all means work hard at improving your standard grammar and spelling, but don't think that your fiction always has to be in a 'British' voice to succeed. After all, Nigeria's Ben Okri won the 1991 Booker Prize with *The Famished Road*, and Chinua Achebe's *Anthills of the Savannas* contains large sections in West African English that are not easy for the uninitiated. The result is a valuable insight into a culture that might otherwise stay closed to outsiders. But for popular rather than literary fiction the basic principle applies – a little dialect goes a very long way.

For native English writers, it is worth remembering that, good as they are, even the likes of E. M. Forster and Paul Scott have been criticised by Indians for not getting Indians quite right. How far you choose to go along the path of writing in a local voice is a matter of confidence in your own ear for the 'otherness' of people and places. Some writers have even developed a style to fit a particular concept of 'abroad'. Jim Crace in *Continent*, the 1989 winner of the *Guardian* Fiction Award, creates a kind of composite Third World landscape and mode of expression that could fit many countries. It isn't easy to pull off, but at least it avoids accusations of not getting a specific place right. There is more about inventing places in Chapter 10.

# 2

# PREPARATION AND SOURCES

The most obvious question the writer must now ask is 'To write a story set abroad, should I have been there?' The short answer is probably 'Yes, or somewhere very like it'. Having said that, however, the last thing you should do is to wait until you actually get there for inspiration to strike. Why not give yourself a head start by doing as much research as possible? That way, you could have several possible storylines or themes in mind before you arrive. But if you are finding the prospect of researching a new location somewhat daunting, this is the time to remind yourself that you probably know a lot already.

## It's your choice

Writers are frequently advised to stick to what they know. This is the time to make a fresh assessment of what you actually do know about a particular place. Much of it may be buried or half forgotten, but wise use of the incredible amount of information available in the form of books and illustrated articles, films, TV, radio or accounts from friends will bring out that kind of hidden knowledge so that it can be polished to add sparkle to your work.

No doubt we have all envied the 'been there, seen it, done it, got the tee-shirt/scars to prove it' type of writer like Ernest Hemingway, Evelyn Waugh or Graham Greene. Not only did they live and work in any number of exotic places, but they were capable of writing about them from the inside out while positively relishing the exoticism and almost inevitable element of danger involved.

But before becoming completely intimidated by this kind of expertise, it is worth remembering that H. R. F. Keating had written at least half a dozen of his highly successful Inspector Ghote novels before visiting India. There must be others in the same position, although they might not be too keen to admit it, and there are certainly many writers who produce strings of volumes set in places they know only from weekend breaks or package tours.

To encourage the writer of lighter work, I will confess to writing a six-part serial set in Tuscany although it had been 25 years since I had last visited Italy, and the nearest I had got to Tuscany was Rome and Venice. In my defence, I would say that I read or reread a dozen or so books, including four guide books (the best being *Tuscany and Umbria* by Tacaros and Pauls, Cadogan Guides series), two art books on the Florentine renaissance, the *Autobiography of Benvenuto Cellini*, Italian cookery books, some Dante, large chunks of *Romeo and Juliet* and assorted travel articles. It was a newspaper article on art thefts in Italy that triggered the idea, and Scotland Yard were helpful about how the Fine Arts and Antiques department operated. Fortunately, I also have friends who know Italy well, but in spite of all this, I still almost came badly unstuck – see Chapter 10, *Avoiding bear traps*.

I also wrote a short story set entirely in Amsterdam's Schipol airport, about an art teacher whose problem pupil goes missing just as the rest of the school party is about to board the plane home. The last time I was in Schipol was in 1965 for a couple of hours on the way somewhere else, but as a former teacher, Van Gogh fan and user of airports, I felt I knew enough to write it. Or perhaps that should be, I knew I *felt* enough to write it. The second rights sold to a Dutch magazine and one day, I really am going to visit Amsterdam properly. So don't be afraid to trade on distant memories and fleeting glimpses, backed up by plenty of checking.

If you are planning a trip to a place you haven't visited before, perhaps for the family holiday, a business trip or to see friends or relatives, start your preparation well in advance. Devour everything you can find on the subject and you should be able to get at least one good plot going before you arrive. It's up to you to provide the best possible seed ground for ideas to germinate. Then you can use the trip to check that you have the details and general feel of the place right and make adjustments where necessary. It will also free you from that feeling of having to think up something complicated and dramatic while you are there and supposed to be enjoying yourself. With that kind of pressure removed, you will probably find more ideas floating gently to the surface, perhaps for something of a quite different length, subject matter or style.

This is exactly what happened to me with a trip to Thailand. I already had the first draft of a serial with me when I went, having done a lot of reading and research. While there, I was able to check the details and generally strengthen it, much to the hilarity of my fellow tourists when they found out what I was doing. They were full of advice as to what to put in and pointed out all kinds of things I would never otherwise have noticed. I got one idea for a short story while there and another when I got back. One sold to *TV Quick* and the other to *Woman's Realm*, and I certainly haven't ruled out the possibility of using Thailand as a background again.

Apart from any other considerations, you will probably find that the more you know about a place before you get there, the more you will get out of the trip personally as well as for your writing. If you haven't considered this kind of intensive preparation, it is worth a try. Simply comparing your expectations with what you find when you get there is an interesting exercise. If you get it right, it gives you confidence to try it again on somewhere else next time, and if you get a few nasty shocks or pleasant surprises, don't waste them. Now you have had that experience, so can your characters.

21

**Where have you been all your life?**

At this point it might be an idea to make three lists. The first should include every place you have ever been to, however briefly, that you consider 'abroad'. For Scottish, Welsh or Irish writers, that could easily be England, and vice versa. This list should include everything, not forgetting day trips to Boulogne, military service, airport transfers, cruise ports, stopovers, and countries you have driven through, or the one you were born in but left before you could walk. Where applicable put in beside each any town, village or district names that stick in your mind from that time. How many of these have you actually used in your fiction, or even considered using?

The second list should consist of places that you have definite plans to visit in the near future. The list might be short, looking no further ahead than next year's holiday, but it should get you moving on the preparation.

The third list is for places you have always dreamt about visiting one day. Pinpoint your real priorities, but take this seriously because it can tell you a lot about yourself. Jot down what attracts you to those places. Is it their beauty, their history and culture, or something about the people? Is it simply the fact that you know so little about them – that they seem mysterious, romantic, 'forbidden' or even dangerous to you?

Taking the lists together, work out what attracts you physically to places and why. Is it the sun, the landscape, the balmy nights, the bracing air, the wind in your face, the sights, sounds and smell of the sea, the clarity of the stars, the food, the open spaces, the bustling street life?

Was there any place you particularly disliked or that disappointed you, and if so why? Again, try to separate the physical and the emotional and see if there is a relationship between the two.

## 'Know thyself'

So says the inscription at Delphi, once famed for its Oracle. To help this mysterious process along, here is a none-too-serious classification system for writers and their relationship with places. I believe writers, as well as other people venturing abroad, fall mainly into the following categories – Celtic, Teutonic, Mediterranean, Florentine or Spartan. It has nothing to do with where you were born, your age or your gender. It is simply how you are.

**Celtic types** go for mists, mountains, moorland, lakes and inland waterways. They freckle easily, never feel happy without a sweater or an anorak and take lots of books they've been meaning to read for years. They wander at will, and don't panic if things don't work out according to plan because they didn't really have one anyway, but they hate creepy-crawlies, especially large foreign ones. They dream often and usefully, and write poetry, but have trouble tying down their subtle, delicate prose when it comes to fiction.

**Teutons** head purposefully for the beach or winter sports. They plan the whole thing like a military operation and need a lot of equipment. Their sun beds, parasols, water skis, sail boards and golf bags snag on luggage carousels, while their laptop computers bleep away at all hours. When not bronzing themselves efficiently, they are climbing every mountain, holing every pot and generally throwing themselves into things with a resounding splash. This never stops them writing ten thousand words of muscular prose a day and charging the whole trip to expenses.

**Mediterranean types** only ever go where it's warm. They sit around a lot eating and drinking wine, get up late, and stroll everywhere. Even making notes is a terrible effort for them and their hotel room is soon as untidy with interesting bits they've picked up as their study is at home. They need prodding and deadlines, or they tend to swim lazily in circles waiting for tiny fish to nibble their toes or perhaps for a ride on a dolphin. They tend towards the humorous or sensual in their writing, but editors should consider themselves very lucky to get anything out of them at all.

**Florentines** feel nervous away from towns, answerphones and fax machines. They love shopping, looking smart and being seen, and their fiction reflects this. Their shoes never pinch and they always carry spare pens and several guide books in their Gucci bags. Many Florentines love art and write about churches, museums and food. Swimming and struggling for inspiration messes up their hair so, like the rich and famous they often write about, the more successful Florentines have secretaries to do it for them.

**Spartans** like discomfort, or at least they prefer it to the company of their fellow travellers/writers. They will willingly cope with awful food, bedbugs, Sudanese bus timetables and cholera as they stagger round yak-like under their backpacks. They never take notes, as these tend to get stolen or eaten by goats, but they remember it all with crystal clarity on to an ancient typewriter when they get back. They are particularly fond of deserts and the Trans-Siberian railway, write experimental novels or SF and often get shortlisted for the Booker Prize.

All a bit over the top perhaps, but what all writer/travellers want is to get as much as possible out of their trip and that needs thorough preparation.

## Maps and atlases

Whoever said that a fiction writer should spend half an hour a day on each of the following had the right idea:

- Pretending to be a child
- Thinking about sex
- Reading poetry
- Doing yoga

To these I would add studying maps. You may have to cut down the time spent on the others, and don't we all, but I only have to spot a name like Desolation Gulch, St Hypolite de Cantaloup or Ouagadougou to start me dreaming. Apart from that, maps are a wonderful source of right-sounding names if you want to invent places.

Maps were originally made almost entirely for rulers by the military and traders, the idea being to know which bits of land belonged to whom, how best to defend and exploit what was yours, and where to acquire some more. Except for pilgrims, most other people sensibly stayed near home.

The Ordnance Survey was once part of the army, but even in the military, the importance of maps and basic geographical homework wasn't always heeded. In the Crimean War, the British army disembarked without proper maps of the area. There were large areas of limestone, which meant a lack of surface water, and thirst soon became a major problem. It was also thought that as the Crimean Peninsula was low lying and much further south than Britain, severe winters weren't likely to be a problem, although today any GCSE pupil could explain about the extremes of temperature produced by large landmasses. (See Chapter 7, Weather or Not.)

First things to note are how far you will be travelling and in what direction, as this affects not just climate (although not always in the way you might think) but also daylight hours and jet lag.

All atlases contain relief maps showing altitude, main rivers and so on, but it's worth getting a really good one that shows everything you might suddenly want to check – summer and winter temperatures, prevailing winds, ethnic and language groups, time zones, vegetation and limits of major crops, geology and minerals, railways, main roads and air and shipping routes. Most airlines provide route maps in their in-flight magazines, which can also be a source of other useful titbits. They are free, and nobody minds if you keep them.

If you live around London, one of the best places to buy maps and guide books is the British Airways Travel Centre, 156 Regent Street, W1. If your work has a historical dimension particularly from 1851 onwards, the Thomas Cook Travel Archive, 45 Berkeley Street, W1A 1EB, has a library and plenty of source material. Membership is free, but a £10 deposit is required. For the really adventurous writer, the Public Records Office in Kew, Surrey, has maps of most parts of the world, but for many holiday destinations it's often easier to wait until you get there for a really detailed local map, and don't forget to bring it home, however battered it gets. Almost any map is better than none to get yourself *au fait* with a place before you get there. I never throw away any map that comes my way, and I have several large boxes full, labelled by continent, just in case.

## Reading it up

Having decided on the place, the next step, if you haven't already done it while making your choice, is to comb through the rival brochures for the same destination and keep the most useful ones, particularly those with good pictures. For ways of using pictures to help your writing, see *Other sources* in this chapter and also Chapter 10. Some brochures like Sunmed's *Go Turkey*, *Go Greece* etc, are full of chatty, anecdotal articles speckled with local colour. Some give more up-to-date information than many guide books.

The library is the next stop, and the Travel section the most obvious place to start. There are so many types of guide books around today that it's worth knowing which ones are likely to be the most use for the kind of story you have in mind.

For something young at heart, right up to date and/or adventurous, I find the *Rough Guide* series hard to beat. Library copies often have interesting stains and weird notes made somewhere hot and sticky by the last user. They have an excellent feel for the tone of a place, with unstuffy but thorough sections on general background, local food, languages, customs and 'in' places. For me, their only drawbacks are the almost complete lack of pictures, and the maps which are few, black-and-white, and not always easy to read. Also good

26

of this type is the Travel Survival Kit series (*Lonely Planet*). These aren't as detailed as the *Rough Guides* but have excellent maps and photos which I find very helpful both for advance planning and as an aid to memory later.

The *Blue Guides* are the ones to go for if you are after architectural details or if your main protagonist is into art, history, archeology or antiquities. Information on which famous paintings are in what church, which squares contain what statues, obelisks and fountains, and the room-by-room accounts of museum contents should be adequate for anyone up to professional level.

On the other hand, if you're more interested in routes, times and distances, the *Baedeker AA Guides* have enough detail for you to organise the tailing of a villain, a midnight escape or an across-town car chase from the comfort of your own desk. I personally don't like their way of writing up places alphabetically rather than according to some kind of route plan or theme, but others might prefer it that way. Route buffs could also try the *Byways of Europe* series which incorporates sections of the local equivalent of OS maps in full colour.

Of the many other guide book series, the ones I find most inspirational from their sheer wealth of interesting snippets are the *Nelles Guides* and the *Cadogan Guides*.

Don't stop at the Travel and Reference sections. Sometimes the most interesting books about a place are in the Geography, History, Archeological or Art sections. For a trip to Israel, Rome, or places where Islam, Shinto or Buddism are the main beliefs, the Religion section can be as useful as anything else for an insight into life in these places. The most useful book I found on Thailand was in the History section (*Thailand – The Lotus Kingdom*, by Alistair Sheare). For a serial with an archeological background based in Tunisia, I got a useful edge to the plot, some interesting detail and a bit of emotional shading from three books about the Fall of Carthage. Training yourself to skim effectively is a great help.

If I find something interesting, I want to communicate it

to the reader, not to 'educate', but to stimulate and entertain. I must admit that my own level of interest is my only yardstick for this kind of research. There is nothing more wasteful of valuable writing time than forcing yourself to wade through worthy factual material that bores you. Drop it and go for something else, like a good novel, a collection of essays or something biographical set in the appropriate place. At this stage the fiction writer should be after inspiration, and that comes from fascination and excitement, not dutiful boning up. That may have to come later when you have decided on a plot and/or a theme, but in the meantime, be a butterfly. Settle only on what takes your fancy and allow it to divert you. Above all, have the confidence to feel that if it diverts you, it will divert someone else.

## Making a geographical profile

A friend who teaches geography suggested in a moment of exasperation at the basic ignorance of many tourists abroad that anyone wishing to visit a country should first have to pass a simple test on it. Questions might include the names of the languages spoken, what the basic greeting and thanking phrases sound like, the main religions/belief systems and ethnic groups, the capital and some major towns, national dishes and famous people. Candidates should also have a rough idea of the main physical features (nearest sea, mountain ranges, large rivers) and key historical happenings.

No one calling themselves a writer should ever be in the position of someone I overheard on a coach in Israel. After listening to our guide's account of the kibbutz system prior to a scheduled visit, she asked her companion, 'What was that word beginning with "k" again, honey?' Then she capped this with 'What language to do they speak here?'

Other sticky moments have included the young man looking at a crucifix in Florence and asking 'Who's the little guy on that thing?' and the woman in a Greek Orthodox church on seeing a baptism by immersion demanding to know why they were bathing a baby in there. At least these people asked questions. One couple in Crete had no idea that the language they were hearing was Greek, and someone else in the Canaries thought it was near Ibiza and so the language must therefore be – Italian.

Unfortunately travelling can play havoc with the nerves, the memory, the attention span, and occasionally the will to live (more of that in Chapter 3). All the more reason then, to have the basic facts about the place already in your head so that you don't have to spend too much time orientating yourself when you get there tired and jet-lagged. That way, you will have a framework nicely in place for slotting in more detailed information and impressions from the start.

To give a specific example, the following would make an adequate basic profile for a popular holiday destination – Turkey. The idea is to have already made notes and absorbed at least this much information before you go. Sources for this kind of basic material might be *The Penguin Encyclopedia of Places*, combined with any general encyclopedia, atlas and guide book.

Turkey is six times the size of England. Most of it is in the shape of the huge peninsula of Asia Minor, although a tiny bit, including most of Istanbul, is actually in Europe. Istanbul, the largest town (9 million people) is no longer the capital, which is now Ankara. Istanbul, under its old name of Constantinople, was once the centre of the great Byzantine (Greek speaking) Empire from Roman times until the infamous Sack by out-of-control Crusaders in 1244.

The next invaders were Muslim Turks from the high interior plateau of Anatolia and beyond who founded the Ottoman Empire and eventually came to rule the Balkans and the near East, including Arabia and Egypt. World War I saw the end of this brilliant, wealthy but often corrupt regime, and the country's greatest hero, Kamal Ataturk, declared a modern republic, even

29

discouraging the wearing of the fez and the veil. Modest dress is still advisable outside beach areas, and particularly when visiting mosques which are the most spectacular in the world. The Turkish language has a lot in common with Arabic but is written in the European alphabet.

A channel of varying width separates Turkey-in-Europe from Turkey-in-Asia, so that ships sailing east from the Mediterranean will pass through first the Dardenelles, then the Sea of Mamara and finally through the Bosphorus to reach the Black Sea. The southern (Mediterranean) coast of Turkey is spectacular, being backed by the Taurus mountains.

Traditionally Greeks and Turks have been enemies, but today there is also friction in the Kurdish areas along the border with Iraq. Currency, the Dinar. Commercial closing day Sunday and, in devout Muslim areas, Friday. Some early closing during Ramadan. Faithful called to prayer five times daily by muezzins from the minarets of mosques (often recorded). Rice, mutton, figs, apricots, pistachios and the usual Mediterranean fruit and vegetables. Wool, carpets, leather, cotton, copper.

**Other sources**

Probably the most useful sources of other material are the quality newspapers and magazines. Over the weekend, the *Observer*, the *Sunday Times* and the *Sunday Telegraph* have excellent travel sections, often with the focus on a particular area. They are often detailed and well written enough to provide both reference and inspirational material. Many dailies also have travel pages, the better ones being the *Daily Telegraph*, the *Independent*, *The Times* and the *Guardian* (in the magazine section on Saturday).

Sometimes a colour supplement or one of the glossies has

a picture, or picture-led feature that can trigger a whole plot in your mind, such as one I noticed in the *Observer* magazine about the British Airways stewardess, Pat Kerr, MBE, who started an orphanage in her stopover time in Bangladesh. I was so impressed that I used the idea of starting a children's home for a serial based in West Africa where I taught for some time, with the heroine as a research worker rather than a stewardess.

As well as collecting maps, keep files of pictures that have caught your eye. It is also worth the odd browse anywhere that you might come across old *National Geographic* magazines. The pictures are stunningly good and the articles often so detailed and anecdotal that it is amazing what you can pick up in the way of background material. It may sound primary-schoolish, but I like to cut out good pictures and paste them on the front of the relevant file. I also make slap-dash collages and pin them above my desk. Many times, I've suddenly seen something in one of these pictures that has made a whole scene come to life. Once it was the symbolism of the pattern on a Turkish carpet hanging outside a shop that triggered a whole story. It could be the style of the local police uniform, or some forgotten detail of a well-known landmark.

Keep an eye open for TV news and particularly documentaries on any area that interests you, and video particularly good parts or even whole programmes if you can. I keep a couple of separate video cassettes just for this, and I am often surprised at what I missed first time. Usually it's something going on in the background – the child in shorts sewn from a flour bag held up by a belt made from a bicycle inner tube; the way the women tie their scarves; types of bedding hanging from windows; makes of car. Not that this is surprising. A study by the Institute of Education showed that most people see only ten per cent of the information in any picture placed in front of them, so you can imagine how much of a film is missed.

Embassies, high commissions and any large firms connected with particular areas are only too happy to weigh you down with information and press releases. While some of this is accurate and useful, an awful lot of it has the whiff of wishful thinking or poetic licence, if not something stronger.

## Building your own reference library

Top of my list would be the best atlas you can afford (see above) followed by a cheap school atlas for speed and to avoid distraction. Next would be Pears Cyclodedia, and various other encyclopedias/dictionaries according to interest and purse. Mine include:

*The Penguin Encyclopedia of Places*
*The Royal Horticultural Society's Encyclopedia of Plants and Flowers* (mainly garden plants but useful)
*The Illustrated Encyclopedia of Myths and Legends* which deals with cultures all over the world
*The Oxford Companions to Art and Literature*
*Brewer's Twentieth Century Phrase and Fable*
*The Cambridge Encyclopedia*
Michelin Motoring Atlases for relevant countries
Dictionaries of quotations, and the *Penguin Dictionary of Saints* (surprisingly handy for local interest, feastdays etc).

I would also include some national and regional cookery books, *Miller's Antique Price Guide* (as recent as possible), and *Art of the Western World* as it is very area-orientated.

A dictionary such as *Chambers Twentieth Century*, which gives word origins, is very useful because it gives an indication as to whether a word might or might not be appropriate for use in a particular exotic/historical setting. To give an example: suppose you look up the spelling for that well-known tropical and sub-tropical flowering bush, Bougainvillaea. *Chambers* says it is named after the French explorer, Louis Antoine de Bougainville, even giving his dates (1729–1811). It is therefore no good using this plant name in any work set before this period. In the manuscript of a historical novel set at the time of Christ, I came across a mention of bougainvillaea in the gardens of Herod's Palace. A check with *Chambers* alerts us not just to the anachronistic name, but also to the possibility that since the plant was named after an 18th-century French Captain Cook, it probably was not known in the Mediterranean area in Roman times. It wasn't. The *Cambridge Encyclopedia* says it is a native of South America, and offers an alternative spelling, 'bougain-villea' with a small 'b'. Meanwhile, *The Oxford Dictionary for Writers and Editors* gives us *Chambers'* spelling but with a small 'b', and *Chambers* itself offers the alternative of 'Bou-gainvillia'. Your editor will decide on the final spelling, but at least you won't have put your foot in it. (For more about Flora and Fauna, see Chapter 8.)

In true Desert Island Disc tradition, I would also assume that no writer would want to be without a Complete Works of Shakespeare, a Bible, volumes of poetry, and possibly the Koran, as well as the usual aids to good English style, such as Fowler's *Modern English Usage* and a thesaurus. Although the only other language I can make myself understood in is French, I also find small Italian, Latin and German diction-aries and assorted phrase books can sometimes be useful, along with *Le Mot Juste, The Penguin Dictionary of Foreign Terms and Phrases*.

## What to take with you

Another good reason for having a thorough geographical profile ready on a sheet or so of paper before you go is that it saves carting too much weight around. Similarly, you'll want to select the one or two maps and guide books best suited to your needs well in advance.

Apart from your favourite note-taking equipment, a cam-era is probably as useful as anything. Camcorders and lap-top computers are a great help, if expensive, and I now find a mini cassette recorder immensely useful for making direct observations and recording typical sounds. Doubtless we will all soon be wondering how we ever managed without them.

# 3

# GETTING THERE

So you've stopped the papers and the milk, stocked up on film and done all your preparation. There is even a storyline or two jotted down in your notebook. You're looking on your trip not so much as a working holiday (we all need a break sometimes) but as a time of renewal and creativity. Whether your chosen location is completely new to you or you've been a dozen times before, something different is going to happen – something, maybe many things, that can be used in your stories. But first you've got to get here.

## Travelling usefully

There is no doubt that travelling for pleasure is not the leisurely business it used to be, or Robert Louis Stevenson couldn't have come up with the one about it being better to travel hopefully than to arrive. For the average Brit these days, getting somewhere else almost certainly involves motorways and airports. RLS might have changed his tune, we tell ourselves grimly, had he ever been stuck in a tailback for hours, only to spend most of the holiday at the airport thanks to an air-traffic controllers' strike or a security alert. How you cope with these things in real life is largely a matter of attitude, and how you use them in your fiction is entirely a matter of skill.

Here are some questions to get you thinking next time things come to a grinding halt. Maybe something you find out about yourself could be used to deepen your fictional characters.

1. On a journey, do you see yourself as essentially passive, taking what comes philosophically, not liking to complain? Or do you need to feel an element of control, however illusory?
2. Is being on the move or in transit something you instinctively enjoy? Or do you just want to get there?
3. What kind of transport do you enjoy most, or like least?
4. Does your preference depend largely on the reliability of that kind of travel, its pace, comfort, novelty or any other factor?
5. Given the time, money and stamina, what journey would you most like to make?

One thing is certain, however: even Gatwick on a bad day is nothing compared to the appalling hardships suffered in the past by unwilling travellers, such as slaves, prisoners or immigrants on long sea voyages, columns of refugees or defeated armies. Before writing about such things, you will want to read contemporary accounts or well-researched novels. Visiting places associated with these experiences can be a very moving experience. That said, for most people today, foreign travel is associated first and foremost with getting on a plane.

**Come fly with me**

Anyone over thirty might remember when flying was considered the most glamorous way to get around. For some people it will always retain that image. From the writer's point of view, however, it does have certain drawbacks, the main one being that all flights on commercial airlines anywhere in the world tend to be remarkably similar. You might get the odd regional variation – palm wine on Nigeria Airways, some praying in the aisles on a flight via Saudi Arabia or a particularly forceful Aeroflot stewardess. But most of the time by mid-flight you are hard pushed to work out which hemisphere you are in, let alone whose air space, especially at night.

A second drawback is that you miss so much, especially that leisurely acclimatisation to new places and faces that almost any other form of travel provides. This is perhaps best summed up by an exchange overheard on a London bus:

> 'We went to Lanzarote last year.'
> 'Where's that, then?'
> 'I dunno – we flew.'

Someone was clearly selling themselves short here, but at least it underlines the need for thorough homework. It also shows that journeys are excellent for eavesdropping – a vice that most writers acquire sooner or later.

On the plus side, there are aspects to flying which can be almost surreal. David Lodge has captured this beautifully at the beginning of *Changing Places*, where his hero on a flight to America surveys the Greenland icecap from a godlike altitude as a tiny ice cube melts in his drink.

Between trolley visits, challenge yourself to find the right words for the changing cloudscape, the maplike look of the ground, the light patterns of cities at night or sunrise coming up over the Sahara from – how high did the captain say? And which town/mountain range is that down there? But it is also a good time to remind yourself that for fiction, mere observation and description are never enough. Concentrate on your *feelings* as you fly, not forgetting to do the same for your protagonist.

One warning as you fasten your seat belt: flying seems to bring out the poet in non-poets. It is surprising how many writers fall into the trap of describing it all beautifully, but in quite the wrong language for the viewpoint of the story.

## Hints for the in-flight writer

- For a good view, ask for a window seat away from the wings.
- If your flying time includes sunrise or sunset, make sure you sit on the relevant side of the plane. It's quite easy to work this out in advance, and you could be rewarded with a spellbinding view.
- Try chatting with your neighbour. As well as lapping up the horror stories which are guaranteed to come thick and fast, you'll get a fresh perception of the trip.
- Use some kind of map to follow the route, even it's only the one in the in-flight magazine.
- Use delays or the flight itself for people-watching. Study reactions, faces, clothes. Listen to unfamiliar languages. Even on a charter flight to the Costa with a couple of hundred like-minded compatriots, try to imagine who they are, their relationships and what they expect to find there.

I have found this last point particularly useful as a trigger for plots and have got at least four short stories out of airport situations. My favourite, *Nowhere Man*, is about the alarming effects of jet-lag on a world-weary business type who has upset the airline staff once too often, and how they get their revenge. There must be dozens of other stories lurking round the airways just waiting to be spotted.

## Exploiting other forms of travel

Something has already been said in Chapter 1 under *Quickening the pace* about using a journey to get the action moving. Every form of transport has not only its own pace, but also its own rhythm, almost its own tune, which those with a good ear for language can exploit to the full. Don't be afraid to go for the unusual. Many travel companies provide opportunities to try local forms of transport, and activity holidays are becoming more popular every year. Consider the table (Fig. 1) and tick how many you have experienced yourself but have never thought to use in your work. Some could well form the main background for an entire story, while others might figure only briefly to move things along, vary the pace or create a mood.

Even a mere taster of the more exotic forms of getting about can be an eye-opener for the writer, and could be used in the most unconventional ways. A friend who once made a parachute jump for charity produced a wonderfully imaginative short story about being a bird. If you'd like to write a

## GETTING ABOUT

### LAND

| *Mechanised* | *Human-powered* | *Animal-powered* |
|---|---|---|
| Car/taxi | Bicycle | Horse-riding |
| Lorry/van | Rickshaw | Pony-trekking |
| Caravan/camper | Roller-skates | Camel/donkey |
| Bus/coach | Skis/sledge | Elephant |
| Motorcycle/scooter | Walking/climbing | Bullock cart |
| Rail | Jogging | Horse and carriage |
| | Hitch-hiking | Gipsy caravan |

### WATER

| | |
|---|---|
| Dinghy/canoe | Wind-surfing |
| Fishing boat | Scuba-diving |
| Cargo ship | Commercial diving |
| Cruise liner | Water-skiing |
| River boat/barge | Swimming |
| Yacht/schooner | |

### AIR

| | |
|---|---|
| Commercial jet | Parascending |
| Private plane | Hang-gliding |
| Helicopter | Parachuting |
| Glider | Ballooning |

Figure 1.

novel set in say, medieval England, nineteenth-century Russia or the American West, try a bullock cart or similar – then imagine that you are pregnant or wounded. For Victorian times, a horse and trap is an experience you shouldn't miss. There are many holiday destinations where horse-drawn carriages or *caleches* are part of the fun, while the view from a camel, elephant or tram offers a whole new perspective on life, past or present.

What is of fundamental importance however, is that the type of transport you include should in some way complement the emotions or general tone of the story. The more exotic the transport, the more essential this is. It doesn't matter if you've been on a yak trek up the Himalayas – it is actually better not to use it at all than to use it clumsily or to 'thow it away' on the wrong story, or the wrong people in that story.

Here are some examples of choices about transport I had to make in two serials, *Lily of the Nile* and *Voice of the Turtle* (both for *Woman's Weekly*).

*Lily of the Nile* is set in Cambridge and Egypt and is about a girl who finds an alabaster perfume bottle in her dead grandmother's belongings. The bottle is eventually authenticated as having belonged to Queen Nefertari, but the contents are even more interesting. When analysed, the residue yields a highly marketable formula for the beautiful queen's perfume. Some family skeletons are also unearthed in the process, so the whole thing has the feel of a race against time – to get the business side set up before rivals get hold of the formula, and to prevent too much emotional damage being done to the heroine's family.

With that in mind, I decided against a Nile cruise as part of the action. Apart from having to follow in the wake of *Death on the Nile*, it simply wasn't appropriate, since the heroine was only there on business and in a hurry for most of the time. Changes of flight plan and hair-raising taxi rides round Cairo were more her style. But we know she is falling for the hero when she finds herself *dreaming* of floating down the Nile with him in a *felucca*. When the hero finally catches

up with her in Luxor, he shows his hitherto undeclared interest by turning up with two camels for a surprise ride to the
Temple of Karnak. Now one hour on a camel had been quite
enough to convince me that two people sharing the same
beast would be utterly inconducive to romance. So the ride
keeps them apart for a little longer (try holding hands on
separate camels). For the way back, they take a *caleche* –
much more romantic than a taxi, but respect for local custom
had to prevail, and real passion has to wait a little longer.

*Voice of the Turtle* is set in London and Turkey. Our heroine's first encounter with the hero is while holidaying on a
*gulet* (Turkish hired yacht) with her family and her wealthy
fiancé. The mood ought to have been romantic/idyllic as they
drift from cove to cove – except that the heroine's fiancé's
attitude is that of slumming it (his father owns a luxury
yacht). In such close quarters, her family is uncomfortable
with him. Her unexpected meeting with a handsome marine
biologist while swimming after a turtle starts her wondering
if she's engaged to the wrong man.

Having done its job by telling us a lot about everyone, the
*gulet* scene comes to an end, and we return to London with a
bump, when our heroine finds that her fiancé's powerful father
(also her boss) is heavily involved in a hotel development that
will wreck the turtle breeding sites. But we know she'll trace the
turtle man again, and that her quest will lead her back. When it
does, she is jobless and broke, and has to cross Turkey by local
bus in winter to reach him. This journey is now a symbol of the
break with her old high-powered business life and of her new-
found freedom from emotional and social restrictions.

## Everything to declare

An inevitable part of travel is the official transit point between one country and another. As customs and other ad-
ministrative barriers come down in the EC and the old
Eastern Bloc, they are getting more complicated and fraught

elsewhere. The drama potential of Berlin's notorious Checkpoint Charlie has been handed on like a red-hot poker to any number of border posts round the world, and while this may not please the traveller, it can certainly be explored by the writer. Consider some of the possibilities. Your protagonist could be:

- coming home;
- entering territory considered hostile in some way;
- hating to leave;
- desperate to get out;
- blissfully unaware of what the reader knows is waiting to pounce;
- carrying something dangerous or illegal, knowingly or unknowingly.

Even if none of the above is helpful to your particular story, there is a certain something about the act of passing from one country to another, and few people remain unaffected by it. Neither should your characters. There could be an ideal opportunity here to tell us something about their strengths and weaknesses. If you recognise any of these responses as you are asked unexpectedly to open your bags, try them on your characters:

- instant paranoia;
- outraged indignation;
- unfocused guilt;
- a knee-jerk attempt to joke or bribe your way out;
- a show of teeth-grinding correctness;
- serene confidence in your own innocence/ability to talk your way out of anything;
- sudden affection for your good old British passport;
- acute awareness that this place might actually be the hellhole Amnesty has been saying it is for years.

## The journey as a metaphor

As mentioned in Chapter 1, the most obvious metaphorical use of the journey in fiction is as a quest of some kind. More often than not, the quest is for self-discovery, or for enlightenment on some aspect of the human condition. The use of such a metaphor can be very obvious, forming perhaps the backbone or heavily influencing the structure of the work. There are very many examples of this, from *The Pilgrim's Progress* to Conrad's *The Heart of Darkness*, the latter so powerful that it was drawn heavily upon for the film *Apocalypse Now*. Other works use the quest metaphor so subtly that the reader is hardly aware of it, but there can be few stories involving a journey where some kind of metaphor is not intended. One nice use is in John Mortimer's *A Voyage Round My Father*.

Apart from a quest or exploration, the journey can also be used to imply a state of transition, of drifting, of existing in No Man's Land, of rootlessness, of not-belonging – where time can be suspended even if movement is not. This is perhaps more suitable for a literary work perhaps than for a commercial short story about a coachload of 'the lads' heading for a revenge match in Belgium. On the other hand, why be bound by the conventional wisdom? What on the surface looks like random mayhem on that coach could in fact be a journey of self-discovery. The real skill here would be in making such a metaphor come alive within the framework of the characters' perceptions.

As for simply walking, most of us have forgotten how, which is why walking holidays are increasing in popularity, from the Dordogne to Nepal. Now there's another story . . .

# 4

## BEING THERE

However good your preparation, and whatever the delights or otherwise of your journey, there is nothing to match that first exciting awareness of being somewhere different to get the creative juices stirring. How you react to this may well be a matter of personality. Perhaps this is why two apparently contradictory pieces of advice are often given to writers in new places. These can be summed up as *Hit the ground running* and *Lie back and let it happen*.

### Hit the ground running

Don't waste a moment. With notebook on knee, camera to hand, recorder in pocket, write down, photograph and record everything from the minute you arrive. In many ways, this is sound advice. You might miss something. You never know what might come in useful, and first impressions are often the most vivid (if not always the most reliable).

I shall always be grateful to the 'old hand' who, on my first day of a two-year teaching post in Africa, advised, 'take all your pictures right now. In a week, you'll actually believe all this is normal.' The human consciousness is very adaptable. It can pass from thunderstruck to blasé remarkably quickly.

**Sit back and let it happen**

Put all your preconceptions on hold. Open your eyes, ears and mind, but not your notebook or your camera shutter – not yet. Give it a while to stand, then skim off the cream. Don't put barriers between you and the immediate experience, and allow intuition to guide you as to what will remain important. If you act like a tourist, or worse, a journalist, you'll be treated like one.

If you remember the *Know Thyself* thumbnail sketches in Chapter 2, you may find that Teutons and Florentines will go for the first option, Celtic and Spartan types for the second, while Mediterraneans might be too busy enjoying themselves to do either. Each approach has a lot going for it. At the extreme, the two are mutually exclusive, but it is possible to alternate them on subsequent trips. A lot also depends on the time available, whether you know the place already and how good your memory is. Then again, on any one trip other opportunities will arise to try out the different approaches. Here are three examples you might like to think about in this context:

1. On a package cruise down the Nile you get talking to the tour guide and he invites you to a family wedding. Do you:
   (a) regard this as your best photo opportunity since Princess Di went walk-about in your town and go with flash bulbs, extra film, tape-recorder and a notebook protruding from your bum bag/multi-pocketed gilet?
   (b) take it as an honour, leave everything on the boat except plenty of local currency, put on your best clothes and prepare to make a night of it – then write it all up in your cabin before breakfast next morning?
2. On a picnic/nature trail/jeep safari, you get a glance of some rare animal or unusual incident. Do you:
   (a) destabilise yourself and your fellow travellers trying to find the camera and get a shot in before it disappears?

45

    (b) lose all sense of time and purpose as you stare in won-
        der at the sight?
3. You are stuck for what could be hours in a crowded
   foreign train or bus station. Do you:
    (a) look for an English newspaper, and failing that, set
        your watch alarm and go to sleep?
    (b) catch up on that novel you haven't had time to open
        yet?
    (c) play people-watching and/or try talking to your neigh-
        bours?

There are no right answers here, but if you are prone to one,
try another for a change. If you go for (a) unhesitatingly
every time, check your fiction for signs of creeping journalism
– and your soul in case it is trying to sneak away.

## What only being there can give you

Improvements in information and audio-visual technology
have been vast, so you may already have a fair idea of what
to expect before you arrive. Many destinations now have
theme parks and museums offering all kinds of potted experiences right down to simulated smells and 'tactile opportunities'. But there are still so many things you can only know by
being there. Other people can tell you what it was like for
them, not how it will be for you. Chapters 5–8 deal with how
to get the most from the more obvious aspects of any location – people, landscape, climate, flora and fauna – but the
next few headings deal with some interesting subsidiary aspects best covered as part of the initial impact of a place.

### The quality of the light

People will sometimes refer to the light of a particular place
as if it is only their mood or imagination that makes it dif-

ferent. There are perfectly good scientific reasons why the quality of light varies round the world and most of them are to do with the thickness and composition of the atmosphere. There will be more about this in Chapter 7, Weather or Not, but meanwhile try this simple test. Compare photos or a film of a place you know with the reality you experienced. What places tend to be flattered by film, and which undersold? In the last twenty years, the quality of film has improved so much that if the camera wants to lie, then it will, and for commercial purposes it usually does.

Sadly, disappointment with the reality is often the result. Some places are hardly recognisable without a blinding blue sky or a stunning sunset. The Pyramids under cloud or in a dust haze? The Taj Mahal in the rain? Santa Sophia sparkling with frost? It happens, so make the most of it in your fiction, even if it isn't quite what you wanted to see. But there will be compensations – tricks of the light that only you were there to see, strange angles, ephemeral effects that even a camera can't capture for you, and which could give your work an edge of originality.

## Night and day

Check daylight length for any place outside our own latitudes with which you are unfamiliar, particularly if you are writing something long enough to span seasons of the year. You can't have the sunset drinks on the veranda at eight in Thailand, or Singapore, or Nairobi or anywhere within the tropics for that matter, because it is always pitch dark by then. Six to seven is the time for sundowners and technicolour sunsets. In March and September, day length is roughly the same throughout the world (twelve hours of each) – hence the term equinox (equal day and night); but watch out for June and December (the solstices) where variation according to latitude is at its most extreme,

A place's latitude is where it is in relation to the equator which is 0 degrees (the lowest latitude) and the north and south poles (the highest, at 90 degrees north and south). To give a small example: we know that in June in Britain (between 50 and 60 degrees north and therefore verging on the high latitudes), it can be light until ten o'clock, but the same won't apply to the Mediterranean areas, which are much further south (between 35–45 degrees as a rule of thumb). It will be dark by eight in, say, Majorca, in June and even earlier at all other times of the year.

But neither do these mid-latitude areas experience our long dark winter evenings. It is worth remembering that New York is on the same latitude as Rome, not London, so don't have your heroine arriving in broad daylight when it should be dark or vice versa. Crime and thriller writers for whom time and darkness can be crucial have to be particularly careful here. If it isn't crucial, and you are not quite sure and can't check it, it is better not to be too specific.

*The hours of darkness*

There are a number of points to be considered here, some obvious, some less so.

1. If you normally live in or near even a small town, you may well have forgotten what real darkness is like. There is such a backglow (street lights et cetera reflected down from the layers of atmosphere) at night over large parts of the developed world that it confuses the wildlife. Almost any holiday destination which isn't a large town should provide you with a chance to think about the quality of darkness and the role it can still play in people's lives. I once asked a young Nigerian student who had just returned from his first visit to England what his main impression was, to which he replied, 'It was never truly night, so I wasn't afraid.' Another example is from a friend who worked in China. The standard-issue light bulb is fifteen watts in many areas, one per room. When she managed to get hold of a 50-watt bulb, people passing

48

her window turned to stare. In short, we in the west take
light too much for granted.

2. Not only is there far less light than we are used to in many
foreign locations, but it takes interesting forms. Firelight,
lamps of various kinds, torches and candleglow are all open
to dramatic, romantic or humorous possibilities, as are the
power cuts and brown-outs that are often a feature of the
most surprising places. If you believe as I do that electric light
has virtually killed the ghost story, now is your chance to
resuscitate it, especially when you notice how even the most
effective kerosine lamp never quite reaches into the corners.

3. Go in for some serious moon-watching and star-gazing.
Film is quite hopeless for this. When did you last see the
Milky Way, a shooting star or a satellite? Do you know
the Pole Star from Andromeda, or your Mars from your
Venus? Ask the local people about the various constella-
tions and you'll get some fascinating replies which might
provide a catchy title or a useful metaphor.

4. Night really does fall quickly in the tropics. On the Equator, twilight can be down to ten minutes. This is because
the earth's circumference is at its greatest here. It works
on the same principle as a spinning top. The surface of the
bulging middle has to move faster than the tapering polar
regions just to keep up. So the equatorial parts are fairly
whizzing past the sun compared with elsewhere. Therefore, as you are sitting with a sundowner on the equator,
it isn't the gin: you are actually moving round to the dark
side much faster than at home. The same applies to dawn,
which takes place at a positively alarming speed in the
tropics but doesn't get so much attention.

5. Many Europeans find it hard to adjust to twelve-hour
tropical nights. We are used to thinking that if the weather
is warm and sunny, then it's going to be light until nine
o'clock at least, so we can do all the things we normally
do at home on a fine summer evening. But when it is dark
at around six o'clock all year, boredom can set in very
quickly. It may be fine for a holiday, but how would your
protagonist cope with this for any length of time?

*Colours of Day*

Most people would probably agree that writing without the mention of colours is like food without spices. Yet writing tutors often set exercises to describe a place or person using no named colours at all. If you haven't tried something like this, it is worth a little of your precious time, because there are several good reasons for this seemingly negative approach to colour:

1. The average reader's capacity to visualise and fill in colour is much better than it was before the advent of quality colour printing and TV. These days it is almost superfluous to state that the Mediterranean is blue, the Parthenon is white, and sunflowers are yellow. So avoid stating the obvious unless your story requires it in some way.
2. There is a temptation to go mad with the paint box just to ring the changes on, say blue – sapphire, turquoise, azure, cobalt, forget-me-not and so on. Whatever esoteric tint you come up with, someone will have got there before you. Lawrence Durrell is one who has almost cornered the market in this respect. My favourite is his skyline of 'hot nude pearl' from *Justine*. It sounds overdone out of context, but it fits the mood of the book. Be as original as you dare, but always in keeping with the tone of your story and avoid tints so obscure that your readers will need a dictionary.
3. How people see colours is very much a matter of upbringing and convention. African students often ask why main roads on maps were red and rivers blue, since it was obvious to them that main roads are blue/black (tarmac) and rivers are red (mud). An extreme case, perhaps, but a reminder that the perceptions and experience of our characters may be very different from our own. I once heard a Nigerian describing an Irish friend as having eyes like Star bottles – Star being a local brand of lager in green bottles, and emerald, jade and the sea being unknown in this area. Result, an original and hilarious simile full of 'local colour'. As for conventions about the significance of colours,

these are so variable as to be always worth checking on
the spot if they are important to your story. White for
mourning in Hindu areas is only the most obvious
example.


*National and regional colours*

I like to make a simple colour profile for any place I visit. I
may not use the colours directly, but it is a great help in
bringing back the place clearly again later. I start it while
there and then tidy it up and file it later. Each entry need be
no more complicated than the following:

- **Crete** – Surprise – rock on south side mostly a warm
  butterscotch/honey, not usual white limestone. Sea colours by shore missing the clear bright swimming pool
  tone of white areas. Dust reddish, almost African. Buildings not whitewashed as Greece – disappointing, shabby,
  peeling dingy green and blue paint. Widows' black looks
  sand-washed, almost charcoal in strong light.
- **Thailand** – saffron robes of the monks. Rice-green.
  Elephants at Mai Sai exact colour of the rocks when dry:
  like slippery mud when wet. Temples all primary colours
  – red, blue, green, jewel bright. Was the Parthenon once
  like this? Wild forest orchids mainly mauve, same colour
  as Thai Airlines logo and uniforms.
- **Italy** – a style riot. Constant contrasts between ancient/
  classical buildings, even whole towns in sienna, umber
  etc. with bright peasant colours of red and green reflecting the national flag, and stylish muted olives and tans
  of expensive clothes. Siena so chic, even the pigeons and
  the cats seemed colour-coded to match the stonework.
- **Israel** – national flag blue. Why? Nothing else was, including sea. Desert colours, with army fatigues torn between stone and olive. Galilee very green after the south.
  Desert colourless at midday. Dead Sea salt dark greyish.
  Modern buildings white/cream.

- **Egypt** – Cairo is uniform khaki. Nile likewise. Holy colour is bright green for flags and neon lights on mosques. Strip lights in garish colours much in evidence. Sand only looks gold in late afternoon. Camels lovely pale buff, lighter than the ones in Tunisia.

The natural colours of a place can change dramatically with the seasons, which must be taken into account if you are going to attempt something over a longish time span. We are quite used to the enormous colour differences between winter and summer in Northern Europe. In most of the tropics, what looks like pale sand can turn tomato-soup red with the rains, and the whole appearance of the place changes dramatically. For more about the changes caused by climate, see Chapter 7.

*Sounds*

Almost all sound registered by the human ear is made directly or indirectly by people, animals or the elements. As there are separate chapters on these, this section deals with general noise levels and sound changes throughout the day.

Countries are like people – the younger they are, the more noise they make, and the older *you* are, the more you notice it. Noise-making devices of all kinds have multiplied in recent years. As a result, the individual sound signature of so many places has been almost lost in the din of traffic, aircraft, next door's telly or ghetto blaster. And is any market day improved by those dreadful street tannoy systems?

Even so, it is always worth taking time out to close your eyes and just listen. Vary the time each day and note the differences as well as your reactions.

- Are the noises and noise levels more or less what you expected?
- When is it quietest, what can you still hear? In hot rural areas, the quietest time is just after midday when everything shuts down. Even the children, dogs, donkeys and

insects have given up, while the hours before dawn seem to rustle, creak and hum and croak alarmingly.

- Which sounds please or irritate you? Would your protagonists feel the same? Don't forget to allow for any age gap.
- Try to imagine what the place would have sounded like a century ago.

'One night in Bangkok,' says the song, 'makes a hard man humble.' Possibly this does not refer entirely to the noise levels, but it just as well might. Substitute almost any Third World city for Bangkok, and the effect is similar. The noisiest night I ever spent was in Lagos, in a modest little hotel situated between the international and domestic airports. Being in transit, I'd thought a stay there preferable to a long taxi journey in the morning. The A1 Tourist Hotel had a pan roof and windows that either didn't close or didn't open. When a plane came over, the beds and enamel wash bucket vibrated, the goats and sheep in the courtyard woke up, and so did every baby, cockerel and dog for miles. There was an open-all-hours panel beater's across the yard, with the car-washing pipe doubling as the public washroom/laundry. On one side was a late evening class chanting the Koran, vying with international wrestling on TV from everywhere else. Whenever the town electricity went off, the hotel generator under our window coughed into action, thereby waking up every goat, sheep, cockerel and baby that had managed to doze off between flights. Outside was a toll booth where drivers stopped, hooting, to have furious rows with the gate keeper. In the odd lull, it was just possible to get the stereo effect of several species of mosquito attacking both ears.

Now the reason for including this personal account of a rough night is to show that not everything can be used for fiction. Polished up, it might be fine for a jokey travel feature on where not to stay in Lagos. For any kind of fiction, however, such an account would have to be:

(a) heavily pruned, as it is far too long and descriptive;

(b) altered to suit the precise tone of the work;
(c) broken up, preferably with dialogue, to show some kind
    of time progression, plot development, or characters' re-
    actions.

Knowing how to angle your material to the kind of fiction
you are writing is so important that the whole of Chapter 9
is devoted to it.

To conclude the rowdier aspects of being on location: on the
plus side the same technological wizardry that can make any
place a noisy nightmare also allows you to take some of it
home with you. As well as using a mini cassette for background
noises, I always try to buy some tapes of local music. Belly
dancing, high-life, steel bands, bazouki music, the local church
or town choir – all can be marvellously evocative on a dark
winter evening when stuck for inspiration at your keyboard.


*Getting touchy*

I once wrote a profile of a Red Cross nurse who had just
returned from Ethiopia. 'They're such *touchy* people,' she
smiled. 'They love to touch you.' The English, as foreign
friends constantly remind us, are not touchy people. Ad-
monished from an early age not to touch, we go through life
with our hands firmly clamped at our sides, while the rest of
the world tweaks, strokes, hugs, pats and pokes to find out
if things are what they seem. This is something nobody can
do for you, and abroad is the best place to practise since it
will not be thought odd. Imagine a French housewife not
squeezing a melon or an avocado before buying. In many
countries, fruit and vegetable sellers offer juicy chunks of
their wares as a matter of course. Buying almost anything in
a market, from leather jackets and jewellery to carpets and
cloth, will involve being told to feel it or try it on. Of course,
it could always be you they are trying it on with, but shying
away from normal physical contact can cause genuine puzzle-
ment and hurt. In the end, you could be the loser.

Holidays are a good time to banish your phobias and make an idiot of yourself in front of people you will never see again. So pat that camel before the ride. Stroke that python at the snake farm when the guide asks for volunteers. Squealing is optional, but usually stops when people find that your average snake is warm, dry and quite pleasant to the touch. Don't forget to touch rocks and building stone. Rock samples, seed pods and shells will give you something tangible to take home (provided they aren't protected or prohibited). In the 1970s, smuggling cloves out of Zanzibar was punishable by death, as a friend who brought me back a handful was at pains to point out. I had some in the kitchen spice rack anyway – but somehow those were special.

In some parts of the world, it is believed that leaning the head on certain rock formations and standing stones induces visions. Try it. It might open up a whole new dimension for you. Tree hugging can also be rewarding for the more imaginative writer. Then there's covering yourself with therapeutic mud, bathing in hot springs, or enjoying a Turkish bath with the Turks. Americans call this sort of thing getting in touch with yourself. You may call it daft, but if a safe opportunity is there for a new tactile experience, why not take it?

## Scent or smell?

The general smell of a place is something that you can't take home and think about afterwards, although individual smells in the form of an oil, perfume or spice can help. As with sound, many places are losing their individual smell signatures, sometimes because of increased hygiene, but more often to the reek of diesel and increased pollution. Perhaps it was this that inspired Patrick Suskind to write his best-selling novel *Perfume*. It is the story of Grenouille, an eighteenth-century Frenchman born into dreadful poverty who can experience the world only through his sense of smell. This surreal descent into weird eroticism and finally murder may not be to everyone's taste, but it is an object lesson to the fiction writer on what can be done with the most neglected of our senses.

Romantic novelists, however, may be happier, in the words of one magazine editor, simply to 'smell the flowers along the way'. Smell then quickly becomes a scent, aura or perfume. Conscious of the need to accentuate the positive and eliminate the negative, beginner writers sometimes attribute exotic perfumes to flowers that don't smell at all. If in doubt, sniff where you can, rub leaves, or check with the list in Chapter 8.

Some people pride themselves on their sense of smell, even making a career of it in the case of wine experts and perfume 'noses'. But even the amateur can have fun trying to describe something new. The best advice in this case is to jot down a note about it immediately. The nose more than any other sense organ becomes very quickly saturated, and next day you may not even notice that elusive whiff that first fascinated you.

### Getting it together

To summarise, *being there* for the writer means four things:

- absorbing the atmosphere – edging your way under the skin of a place – so that anything you choose to set there will feel right;
- looking for something, however apparently insignificant, that could trigger a plot, enliven a character or deepen the integrity of your work;
- checking what you already know or think you know;
- getting all this down as effectively as possible.

A cautionary tale often told at writers' gatherings is of the woman who wrote an ecstatic one-liner in her journal: 'I'll never forget today.' But then of course, she did. Indeed it can't be stressed often enough what a fickle thing is the human memory. Whether you are the *hit the ground running* type or more of a *sit back and let it happen,* get it down you must.

Some writers keep only a journal and write everything up on a day-to-day basis, sorting it out when they get back. Others prefer the three-notebook approach. The first is tiny enough for the shorts or back pocket when freedom is all, the second is a reporter's ringback for other occasions, and lastly comes an A4 pad kept back at base for when inspiration really strikes. Together with some cardboard wallets for the notes you brought with you and material you collect, this is usually sufficient. There is more about this in Chapter 10 under *Finding it again.*

A couple of days before going home, run a check. Have you:

1. Made enough notes and asked enough questions?
2. Bought plenty of postcards in case your photos are a wipe-out? Bought local slides and music tapes? Checked for tourist/promotion videos? These are often better than most amateur work.
3. Got more maps and leaflets than you started with, however travel-stained?
4. Picked up some cheap locally made bits and pieces at the market that will travel, including food and drink?
5. Sorted through your whole magpie collection and kept only what is most evocative?

Of course you haven't. Nobody's perfect, and this is meant to be a holiday, for goodness' sake. But this is your last chance.

# MEETING THE PEOPLE

The next few chapters are devoted to very specific aspects of any location: people, landscape, climate, flora and fauna. The aim here is to encourage writers who might otherwise miss out on exploring the full potential of a place. Very often the problem is merely lack of confidence, either in one's own knowledge or in the ability to interpret and use that knowledge in the most effective way in fiction writing. So if you always sat at the back in geography, these chapters are for you, starting with the key element in fiction – people.

## The human factor

Something has already been said in Chapter 1 about the difficulties of using major characters who do not share your own cultural background. If you are a beginner tackling a full-length work, it is probably better to use local people only in minor roles unless your knowledge of a place and its people is long-term and extensive. With a short story, however, it is often possible, with careful observation and a fair degree of sensitivity, to make a local person the main character. This can be particularly effective when the theme of the story is something like the effects of tourism or the imposition of the writer's own culture upon a particular location. It is also possible to take some universal topic – jealousy, greed, widowhood or similar – and approach this from another culture's point of view. Even so, this kind of thing can still be very difficult to sustain effectively at length, so a short story is probably a good place to start.

To give an example: on holiday in Minorca I happened to notice that water had to be brought in by lorry tanker every week to the private villas. After filling the cistern the water man sometimes stayed for a drink with the Spanish families, but the foreigners didn't quite know what to make of all this. It struck me that the water man, who often had to go round the back to reach the roof tank, must sometimes see things that would surprise or shock him, and slowly a story began to take shape. It was called 'Villa Rosa' and sold here and abroad. The point is that although the story was from the viewpoint of Luis the water man, the reader's sympathies are also engaged by the lonely Englishwoman in the villa. And how will they both behave when it sinks in that the lover she has been expecting to join her hasn't plucked up the courage to leave his wife?

There is a lovely image in Elsbeth Huxley's *The Flame Trees of Thika*. She describes the very different lives led by the white colonials of Kenya and the local Kikuyu people as being like separate circles, touching only occasionally. With a sensitive writer like Huxley, this means much more than mere day-to-day contact. What the fiction writer is looking for is this extra dimension, where emotional content and impact are involved. A story springing from this sort of contact is bound to be far more satisfying than one where the local people are confined to the traditional 'gofer' roles of waiters, officials or taxi drivers.

This isn't to say that using people simply as 'walk-on parts', or even as props, doesn't have a place in fiction. When it comes to setting a scene, writers can learn from photographers. Keen photographers know that getting a human figure into a shot for scale, interest or colour can greatly enhance their work. Sadly this isn't always easy because people in many parts of the world have an aversion to being snapped unawares by strangers. Sometimes they will overlook the intrusion if a small fee is forthcoming, but for the photographer, the result is often unsatisfactory.

The writer has an advantage here. On paper, people can be placed at will, where and when they are required, to add a human dimension to any scene, create the right mood or sharpen expectations.

## People-watching

If you do wish to incorporate people from another culture in your work, then it is only a matter of courtesy and common sense to get it as right as you can. People-watching starts at the nearest street café. Again, the British are at a disadvantage here, having been taught at an early age that it is rude to stare. Almost everywhere else, it isn't. Even watching other people staring is interesting because the techniques are so variable.

From the comparative neutrality of a street café you can watch people at their most sociable – eating and drinking, greeting and arguing. It is an ideal opportunity to study body language, remembering of course that here everyone is on, if not their best behaviour, at least their second-best behaviour. Better still, pick a place with music. You may then get some dancing and singing, traditional or otherwise. Working out which part of the body people dance from is fascinating, because it varies from culture to culture. It might be the hips, the shoulders, the knees or the feet. And of course, if it's *that* sort of place, you may even get a fight and observe how they go about that, too.

Airports and bus and train stations are also excellent places to watch the general give and take of life. People are more tense when travelling, so allowances have to be made for this. But what is really useful about these places is that they provide the best opportunity most of us are likely to get of seeing people, other than the nearest and dearest, asleep. And sleep they do – in familial heaps, on total strangers' shoulders, sprawled, slumped, open-mouthed. It's the vulnerability that is so appealing. I found myself rethinking one of my characters comprehensively after seeing someone like him sound asleep on an airport bench.

Attitudes to queueing, officialdom, fairness, delays, pick-pockets, tipping – all will be laid bare if you sit around for long enough. You might think the biblical stories about Pharisees demanding the best places are no longer applicable, until you spot the local 'big man' on the move with his en-tourage in a country where democracy is a recent concept and elections are coming up.

On the whole it's better not to be too judgemental. People in the western world are very good at hiding motives, emo-tions and reactions, to the point of downright hypocrisy as far as those from non-western cultures are concerned. When it comes to your characters, however, you can make them as forthright and judgemental as you like. But be warned – many authors are annoyed to find that readers then regard some feisty character's politically incorrect views as the author's own. Sometimes, of course, they are right.

## Town and country

It is a commonplace to say that city dwellers anywhere in the world behave differently from their small town or rural cousins. The corrupting influence of the capital on the 'hick from the sticks' is a well-worked theme, but none the less valid for that. Below are some more town versus country themes. If you yourself have experienced anything similar on your home patch, why not apply this empathy to the people around you while on location?

- Small-town boy/girl makes good in the wicked city, but success is spoilt by the shame felt and shown towards the humble family back home.
- Country girl/boy is forced away from home by prejudice or poverty yet finds a degree of fellowship, love or lib-erty among the seeming degradation of the urban slums.

- Spoilt city slicker learns humility and inner peace (or gets his comeuppance) while in search of his country roots.
- Variations on the Cinderella/Dick Whittington or rags-to-riches theme as country mouse conquers urban loneliness and despair to win fame and fortune.

Some of these may sound hackneyed and rather *passé*, and would have to be toned down if applied to contemporary Britain. But in many developing countries this kind of thing is happening all around, and the experience is still as raw there as it was here a century ago.

Because it is especially relevant to the sections that follow, it might be as well to look at this last point more thoroughly. As in the case of urbanisation, what we are seeing in many parts of the world today is not unlike our own recent and not-so-recent past. This applies not just to living conditions, but to attitudes, skills, social structures and so on. Anyone interested in human growth and development, and that must surely include the fiction writer, can learn a lot by applying this principle wisely. I heard one historical novelist advising another, 'If you want to know what the Middle Ages smelt like, go to rural China.' It is probably what our Middle Ages *felt* like too, especially for the poor and women in particular.

One of the most famous opening lines of a novel is from L. P. Hartley's *The Go-Between*. 'The past is a foreign country. They do things differently there.' Try turning this on its head. Some foreign countries *are* the past. They are all our yesterdays, when things were very different from the way they are now.

## Religion and customs

A case in point is attitudes to religion. Singling out certain places and specific religions would be invidious – and in extreme cases positively dangerous, as Salman Rushdie has discovered to his cost. While it would be ridiculous to claim that religious bigotry and superstition have been eliminated from some western cultures, it is certainly true that the hold religion once had on minds and hearts has slackened considerably. But it is because religion still plays such a powerful part in the emotions, motivation and social fabric of other societies that trying to understand it is so important.

Reading up on the basics and visiting places of worship while abroad is a must. Churches, mosques, temples and synagogues are often the oldest and most beautiful buildings around. For this very reason, the best are on the tourist run anyway. However, it is one thing to gaze in awe at the dome of St Peter's or the Blue Mosque, but quite another to creep into a small parish church or back-street temple and watch things working at grass-roots level. Most religions worthy of the name and, more crucially, the guardian of a particular sanctuary, will accept your interest graciously if you are genuine and respectful.

It is often worth timing your holiday to catch some particularly spectacular religious festival. Sometimes it is difficult to spot where national, regional or civic pride takes over from religious fervour on these occasions. Trying to spot the join is half the fun. Apart from providing an enjoyable opportunity to see the place and the people *en fête*, festivals can be a wonderful backdrop for all kinds of goings-on, with the concluding fireworks always useful for drowning out the bank-vault drilling, shots, or sighs of love.

It was my sister's account of a patron saint's feast-day in an Italian hill-town that provided the background and much of the plot for a six-part serial called *The Feast of Santa Felicita*. Bull-running in Pamplona, the Mexican Day of the Dead, Venetian masked balls, the Rio Carnival – these and others have been used to great effect. And who could resist a Thai festival called The Night of the Hungry Ghosts? Of course, there is always the danger of the 'If it's Siena, let's give them the Palio' type of writing. Looking for something out of the ordinary or using the clichéd in an unclichéd way has to be the best policy.

I learned a valuable lesson from a writer friend just back

from a package holiday in Egypt. When asked if he had found it useful, he said it had been absolutely inspirational – he'd got invited to two Egyptian weddings and a Sudanese one that went on all night. He didn't mention the Pyramids all evening.

## Relationships

Relationships are central to most fiction writing, and the one between the sexes is probably top of the list. If you find the subject fraught in your own cultural context, it will certainly be more so when it comes to other cultures. Even living abroad can leave the outsider very much in the dark, to the extent that some expats, particularly in the Far East and Africa, maintain that they know less after twenty years in the country than they thought they did after two.

If you are truly determined to crack another culture's secret codes and write about it, the only way may be to marry and have children in that culture. A little drastic perhaps, and even then, it could only be a particular class of that society that is opened up to you.

Failing that, if you are still thinking of writing to some extent from the inside, it is advisable to get a good sociological or anthropological study from a specialist bookshop or university library before you go, or while there. This may sound daunting, but a thorough study by experts will highlight any significant gaps in your knowledge. Similarly, novels by local authors are often more readily available on the spot, and can reveal much that tourists never see.

One thing that anyone truly interested in human relationships soon appreciates is Kipling's wry observation that all the people like us are We, and everyone else is They. Deep down most of us still believe that our way of seeing the world is the only valid one, and nowhere is this more true than over relationships. When we don't know, or can't know, we simply assume that things are pretty much as they would be for us. To give just one example: most Western women would find it quite unacceptable to be someone's third or fourth (concurrent) wife. They would then on that basis make all kinds of assumptions about the relationships in a polygamous household.

As a way of challenging your own assumptions (always a useful experience of the writer) consider the list below, and being brutally honest with yourself, jot down your reaction to each:

- Being allowed more than one wife (or husband) yourself.
- Knowing that if your coming baby is a girl you will have to abort her or kill her at birth.
- Having a spouse chosen for you by your parents.
- Not being able to divorce your spouse, no matter what.
- Realising that if your sick husband dies, you as a widow will be entirely dependent on your children and his relatives.
- Accepting that the punishment for adultery is death – probably yours if you are a woman – by stoning.
- Being so hopelessly in debt to a grasping landlord that you have to choose which of your daughters to sell into prostitution.

Some of these are pretty hard to swallow, and there are worse. You may count yourself lucky not to have to deal personally with such things, but they are the stuff of high human drama and still concern a large part of the human race – maybe the smiling people in that last village your coach went through. Simply thinking about such issues can concentrate the mind usefully on long forgotten fears, tensions and emotions.

## Society as a whole

Apart from individual relationships, the fiction writer wishing to probe beneath the surface of a community must also consider it as a whole. This could be on a very local scale, such as a particular town, tribe or district, or be much broader, such as the world of Islam, the Spanish, the American West and so on.

These pointers might help if you are wondering where to start:

- What is the system of government? How much say do the people have in their own affairs and are they happy about it?
- What are the vertical divisions within the society (caste, class etc)? Upon what are they based – heredity, merit, wealth or crude physical/military strength – and in what proportions and combinations?
- Is the society racial or ethnically mixed and to what extent does this mixture play a part in people's perceptions and expectations?
- To what extent is the society open, curious and welcoming to outsiders? Where is the invisible line that says 'Thus far and no further?'
- How are the perceptions, experiences and expectations of the people different from your own?

In Chapter 2 it was suggested that you make a geographical profile for your chosen location. If that includes getting under the skin of a place and using local people in any kind of depth, then it might be an idea to make a sociological profile also – a people profile – using the above points as guidelines and including any instances you come across that illustrate the ways things tick. For serious people-watchers, a special notebook for the little details of human behaviour can be very helpful. The random jottings can then be combed through for anything relevant to the work in hand.

Here are some from my own notebook:

- Italy – rude to ask people how they vote.
- West African cattle nomads – rude to ask how many cows they have, but good manners to inquire after the herd's health.

- In South and Central Africa people tend to try to pass in front of you in a tight spot rather than behind. Seems rude, but is politeness (seen as reassurance that you will not be stabbed in the back).
- Denmark – host husband or guest male expected to pour the tea.
- In Arab countries the way most European women tackle a belly dance when invited is considered highly vulgar because the feet are spread too wide.
- Asked by a visiting teacher to imagine snow by drawing their village sprinkled with sugar, African infants drew neat little cubes all over. They'd never seen granulated sugar.

I don't know if I'll ever use these or the pages of others like them, but they certainly make life more interesting, and who knows what might suddenly spring one day from such titbits?

## Inside story

There are few things more seductive, more conducive to making one want to read on, than the feeling of being let into a secret. Inherent in all good fiction is a kind of contract – come with me and I will show you something new, a hidden treasure, a private world. A good writer learns to create this effect. For the more literary writer, there is that indefinable *voice* that is impossible to teach or to force which proclaims straight away that here is an authority, a person in the know. All the reader has to do is follow.

But there are other ways of creating that aura of authority so vital if the reader is to feel in safe hands for the journey. It is often said that God is in the detail, and for those little snippets that have the ring of authenticity, there is nothing to beat getting people talking.

In some places this is easy, especially where English is easily understood. It also helps if your hosts are not totally fed up with tourists and the society is open and friendly. But where these don't apply, some real effort is required. It is also possible that the more closed the society, the more curious about the outside world and desperate for contact its members might actually be – in which case, the following could be helpful:

- Sticking to the same bar/café, taxidriver/guide/tout/ shopkeeper is better than hopping around for making contacts.
- Come clean and say you are a writer – but don't mention the word 'journalist'. The former is often treated with surprising respect, while the latter may inspire anything, from derision and stone-walling to a knock on your hotel door at two in the morning from the secret police.
- Look out for the local 'experts'. They may not always be accurate or fair, but they will give you something to check and provide another perspective.
- Almost everyone is open to a genuine personal interest and this should include you – so expect to 'tell all' in return. It is only fair and can be a lot of fun.
- Keep your promises, and be generous about help received – a few drinks or a meal, a farewell present or a good tip, exchanging addresses, help with their English, buying something from their shop, et cetera.

In general, the more different the culture, the more trouble people have guessing your age, and some light-hearted guesswork can be a good starter. In many cultures, status increases with age, and people often feel more comfortable when they can see you in relation to someone in their family – mother, grandfather, daughter, et cetera. On a three-hour bus ride in Turkey, the young man beside me poured his heart out about his love life and family problems once he realised I had a son his age. He actually thanked me for listening, because he could never have been so frank with his own mother. Having certain occupations and interests can also help. Football fan, war veteran, nurse, gardener, poet, train-spotter – find another and you're off.

Another good ice-breaker is to produce a mini-cassette recorder and demonstrate by playing back your own voice. As with Polaroid cameras, the secret lies in the immediate pay-off. Many people have never heard their own recorded voice, and few can resist. They say that the sight of a camera turns everyone into film stars. A recorder turns them into politicians or comedians. It doesn't matter if you don't understand a word of it. The sound of their voices can bring a whole day back, even years later. If you want to record your guide's talks, it is only courtesy to ask, and refusals are rare. Recording secretly is a matter for your own conscience.

## Another man's moccasins

If you are familiar with the American Indian prayer 'Great Spirit, let me not die until I have walked for one day in another man's moccasins' – then you will already be aware of its significance to the fiction writer. Like most prayers, it requests the impossible, but the grace is in the asking.

It is often said that most fiction is to some extent autobiographical – that ultimately writers are expressing various aspects of themselves and their experience of the world. The other side of the coin is that any writer who sets out to create characters has to be able to see outside his or her own consciousness and frame of reference. Imagining yourself in someone else's shoes can be a useful part of this difficult process. When that someone else is from a different cultural background, the exercise becomes far more challenging.

So even if you have no ambition to write a story from the viewpoint of another culture or to incorporate local people in the plot, never ignore the various levels of human activity round you, whether you are in a French market or on a slow boat to China. The pay-off can be surprising – whole new insights into the human condition, and a surge of creativity along paths you only half guessed were there.

## 6

# UNDERSTANDING THE LANDSCAPE

It is probably true to say that before the Renaissance nobody thought to look much under the human skin unless they were up to no good. Much the same applied to the landscape until the mid-nineteenth century. Thanks to the work of geologists and geographers like Lisle and Wallace, a great deal is now known about the earth's structure and development. The way people see landscape depends very much on what they understand about it. But this isn't suddenly going to turn into a geography textbook: the aim is simply to encourage you to use unfamiliar landscapes effectively in your writing.

## Changing attitudes to the natural world in fiction

As with much else, how landscape is used in fiction mirrors improved educational standards and attitudes over all. The four main stages are summarised below. What is interesting is how recently the significant changes have occurred.

### 1. From the earliest literature to around 1800

The natural world, including landscape, was simply *there*. It was something to be farmed, mined, climbed only if necessary, and generally coped with to make a living. While its beauty or ugliness might sometimes have been noted, even this was seen as functional. Beauty was there to reflect the goodness of the Creator, and ugliness or destructive forces to show His wrath. That is not to say that this kind of thinking didn't produce some wonderful literature. In fact it produced some of the best. After all, Homer, Chaucer, Dante, Shakespeare and those who gave us the King James Bible all thought of the natural world in these terms.

## 2. The Eighteenth-Century Enlightenment and Romanticism

The complex changes in human thinking generally termed the Eighteenth-Century Enlightenment produced not only the first real novels, but developed the concept of nature as a moral force in its own right. Climbing mountains, sea bathing, exploration and healthy walks were seen as suddenly good for body and spirit – and indeed they were. This was the time of the Romantics, and writers such as Wordsworth, the Shelleys, the Brontës, Tolstoy, Flaubert and Hugo tended to use dramatic landscapes as a rich, abiding, almost living presence in their work.

## 3. Twentieth-century Realism

As with Darwin's theory of evolution, it took a surprising time for the information produced by the new earth sciences to penetrate both the literary establishment and society at large. By the time it did, two things were also becoming clear. Firstly, we seemed to be destroying our environment almost as fast as we were discovering new things about it. Secondly, Nature did not appear to be on anyone's side except its own and we were part of it whether we liked it or not. Poets and writers veered between optimism and pessimism – from Stevie Smith's stark 'I do not care for nature: she does not care for me', to a slap-happy belief that everything would be all right in the end because of the Earth's newly appreciated regenerative powers.

## 4. *Towards the twenty-first century*

Of the various fiction genres, it seems that only science fiction and fantasy/horror have really tried to address these issues in a truthful or original way. An awful lot of fiction, and not just romantic fiction, remains in a kind of Romantic time warp. Maybe this is what the bulk of the reading public still wants. There was a brief flirtation with conservation and ecological themes in the 1970s and briefly into the 80s, but many mainstream publishers and script editors now regard ecological or conservation themes as somewhat 'unsexy' or 'preachy'.

Many writers will be content to leave it like that. The market is the market after all. Having had the second rights for a serial turned down by a Scandinavian magazine, which often takes my work, on the grounds that it was 'too Green', I have had to take the point myself. But for those who would rather lead than follow, perhaps the definitive Earth novel is just waiting for you to write it.

Meanwhile, using the natural landscape as a backdrop in fiction continues to be as popular as ever and, as with almost everything, knowledge is power. The more you know and want to know, the more truthful and effective your work will be.

**As old as the hills . . .?**

One thing generally comes as a surprise to those whose first love at school was not geography, or whose last brush with a map was coping with the Michelin Guide detour to that elusive restaurant. It is the question of the *age* of a landscape. Of course everyone knows that most landscapes are almost inconceivably old in human terms. What is forgotten is that they are not all the *same* age. Somewhere in our collective subconscious there still lurks the creation myth common to so many cultures that it all happened a long time ago, and more or less all at once. 'As old as the hills' is itself one of our more venerable similes-turned-clichés.

However, not all hills are the same age. For example, beside the Scottish Highlands, the Alps are positively spring chickens. When you know the signs, you can actually see it, just as you can with humans.

Neither is it merely a question of comparative age. It took the all-too-unsung genius of W. H. Davies to develop the concept of an entire landscape going through stages, so that it is now possible to recognise young, mature, old-age and even rejuvenated landscapes. You don't have to go abroad to find them, but it helps – because the examples from the British Isles are on rather a small scale. In other places you get the effect in full panavision, and it is much easier to spot.

A good rule of thumb is that the higher the mountains, the younger they are. All the main mountain ranges – the Alps and their extensions into the Atlas of North Africa and right through to the Himalayas, the Andes and the Rockies – consist of great folds in the Earth's crust thrown up by immense subterranean pressures. Mountains like these are simply the result of the very latest upheaval in a series going right back to the time when the crust first began to cool. They are in fact the teenagers of the geographical world, and show frequent signs of youthful instability, such as landslides, avalanches, flash floods and earth tremors.

Not only are these particular ranges young, but the rocks of which they consist are young too, and comparatively soft. Chalk, clays, sandstones and limestones are almost invariably signs of youth. Fossil remains of marine animals embedded in them show that the vast majority of these rocks were laid down beneath seas that have vanished only recently in geological time. Because of their height, they are also often snow-covered for at least part of the year.

Consequently, these young mountain ranges all look rather similar. Sometimes even experienced geographers can't tell them apart purely from photographs unless there is the odd Swiss chalet, Mountie, llama or yak lurking in the background. Beauty apart, they have a kind of raw, unfinished look and feel to them which can be a wonderful source of metaphor. And if an expert can hardly tell his Alps from his Andes or Himalayas, it is reasonable to suggest that if you are familiar with any one of these young mountain ranges, you could stretch this to at least some basic background material for any of the others.

### ... And even older

If some of the best-known mountain ranges are young, others, such as the mountains of Scotland, Wales, the Middle Rhine area or the Appalachians of the eastern USA, are middle-aged. The rocks also tend to be older and similar, so it then comes as no surprise to find coal and iron ore worked in the Appalachians by migrants from Europe who did the same back home and named their new lands for the similarities they found.

Someone said rather cruelly about Canada that it would be fine when it was finished. Possibly they were thinking only of the west side with the Rocky Mountains, or perhaps of human additions to the scene. However, eastern Canada presents a vastly different picture. It is indeed 'finished' in geological terms at least, to the point that it is termed a senile landscape. Most of it is a vast slab of ancient rocks (some of them among the oldest on earth) once also folded and refolded, but very much earlier, and now worn down to the last lumps and bumps until practically flat. The feel is totally different. It is not even the same kind of flatness as the Prairies in the middle of the continent, and invites the writer to respond with appropriate imagery.

The same is true of much of Australia, most of Africa south of the Sahara, large chunks of Brazil and the triangular wedge of India. There is no real equivalent of these vast, immensely ancient, worn down surfaces in the British Isles, or even in Europe. Add the rusty red/orange that aeons of tropical weathering has produced, and the impact is over-whelming – to the visiting European at least. It can seem like a landscape from Hell, or from Mars, alien and intimidating. It can conjure a time out of mind, of being in at the beginning of things, enduring, beyond age or death. Patrick White, the Australian Nobel Prize-winning novelist, made brilliant use of this aspect of his native landscape in *Voss* and, at a more popular level, so have Nevil Shute and Colleen McCollough. There are fascinating tensions to be explored here, between the newness of modern Australian culture and its ancient set-ting. Then there is the way in which the native cultures of these areas chime with the ancient surfaces while having to come to terms with invasions from elsewhere.

In a sense, such senile landscapes have nowhere to go but up – which occasionally happens when earth movements ac-tually force them up *en bloc*. This is known as rejuvenation, and the rivers then all start to erode down again furiously to keep pace, creating the world's mightiest waterfalls in the process. A waterfall is always a sign that rejuvenation has taken place, and the very terms suggest a rich source of meta-phor.

## Under the volcano

It has been said that nobody who has looked into an active volcano is ever quite the same again. The feeling that good old *terra firma* is anything but, does not go away easily, and the mere presence of a volcano in the offing, even a dormant one, fairly rumbles with all kinds of wonderful symbolism that many writers have exploited. Again, it isn't something one can experience by staying at home, unless home happens to be somewhere like Iceland, Naples, Tokyo or halfway up Mount Etna.

Volcanoes, as one local wit put it after the Mount St Helen's catastrophe, are Nature's way of telling you to move. This makes it all the more fascinating to explore the motives of those who continue to live in their shadow, or in earth-quake zones where underground forces are moving whole continents with an inexorable power that leaves faith's ability to move mere mountains on the sidelines. Or does it? You are the writer, and you know your characters better than anyone. Maybe for you or for them, faith conquers all.

Space forbids more exploration of other landscape features such as rivers and glaciers, along with the host of features associated with them. But perhaps this very sketchy outline has served to awaken your interest in landscape. At least it is a reminder that landscape need not be just a static backdrop. Each landscape has a dynamic character all its own which, properly understood and exploited, can create a theme in itself, or underpin one – or simply become a source of inspiration to both you and your protagonists. It is always worth a little extra reading, particularly if there is some striking physical feature on your itinerary that you feel you could use in your work.

**Deserts**

Having had to omit so much in the way of dramatic land-scapes, it may seem strange to single out deserts for a closer look. The reasons for this are threefold.

1. Until fairly recently, deserts were hardly on the regular tourist beat, except for the view from a Nile steamer or the obligatory trip round the Pyramids on a fractious camel. Today, however, the tourist industry in places such as Israel, Tunisia, Morocco, Jordan, Arizona and Australia are well aware of the lure of the desert, and excursions by Land-Rover or camel are part of the fun.
2. Of all landscapes, deserts are probably the most misunderstood. If you fall for their distinctive appeal, they will repay a little time and effort handsomely.
3. From Biblical times, the desert has been a wonderful

source of symbolism, metaphor and romance – sometimes to the point of cliché. In view of what we know today, there is no need to stick to the time-honoured view of deserts. Not all of it was correct anyway, and there are always new ways of looking.

So let us look at some of the popular misconceptions about deserts. Firstly, deserts are not all sand. Only ten per cent of the world's desert surfaces present the classical image of sand dunes. But that is what the tourists expect, so your dutiful tour leader will head for the nearest thing that looks like a dune and run you up and down it. In fact most deserts consist either of huge expanses of almost bare rock with an occasional dusting of sand and patches of sharp, angular stones or of huge expanses of bare rock with a thin scattering of scrub. They are anything but photogenic, especially in the glare of midday, and many desert plateaux rank among the most monotonous and soul-destroying places on earth.

It is only where there is some interruption of the general flatness that you get anything in the way of interesting scenary. The interruption is usually in the shape of former water courses cut into the plateaux (wadis or canyons) or geological accidents such as fault lines and particularly hard bands of rock. Then the results can be spectacular indeed – as in the Grand Canyon, the Dead Sea area, Monument Valley or Ayres Rock. These tend to be the exception rather than the rule and the only time much of the rest looks any good at all is when the shadows are long and the glare is reduced, such as sunrise, sunset or before a storm.

Another belief that has been exploded of late is that deserts are entirely natural – that they show Nature at its most harsh and uncompromising. It is more accurate to say that vast areas of desert are a result of human mismanagement. Rather than Nature not giving Man a chance, the reverse is the case. This is particularly true of Old World deserts like the Sahara. In fact the American and Australian deserts which have suffered less from human interference often surprise European visitors because there is so much vegetation around.

Admittedly it is of the scrubby, salt-bush type, but New World deserts do not fit the stereotype of vast areas of sand punctuated by clumps of date palms.

Neither is it true that when you've seen one desert you've seen them all. Each of the great deserts has characteristics very much its own, including distinctive plant and animal life. It is fairly well known, for example, that only the American deserts have cacti. For camels, it's a case or one hump or two, or no camels at all, but it certainly doesn't stop there. Look out for local specialities in the shape of rock formations, other physical oddities and freak weather. From folklore and human adaptations you could be rewarded with a wealth of fascinating and unique material.

## The desert as metaphor

Similarly, the emotional responses triggered by deserts can be remarkably varied, even contradictory, and therefore likely to interest fiction writers. In studying the list below it is worth noting that deserts are particularly useful as metaphors for *paradox* and *contrast*. Exploring such elements that often lie at the 'dead heart' of these fascinating places can tease the mind away from the clichéd and into something deeper.

- The Wilderness – a place for mad prophets, hermits and seekers after truth, where the lost soul can find itself, but where fools stray from the path at their peril.
- Places of intense quiet, where muffled stillness and peace is all. Yet night cooling can split the rocks with sounds like rifle shots, while the unceasing wind plays havoc with the nerves, whistling into crannies or howling like a demon in distress.
- Symbolic of Hell itself for midday heat, but where the unwary can freeze at night.
- As a metaphor for aridity and barrenness of soul and body. But then comes miraculous fertility when the desert blooms after rain or an oasis provides welcome relief.

- The home of mysticism, hidden knowledge and the mirage – yet nowhere is the air closer, the stars brighter or the land more rawly exposed.

To get yourself in the mood, or to recapture it, try some of the great desert writers, starting with the Old Testament prophet Ezechiel in the Valley of the Dry Bones and working through to *Wind, Sand and Stars* by Antoine de St-Exupéry and T. E. Lawrence's *The Seven Pillars of Wisdom*. But perhaps the ultimate in desert contrasts has to be seen on a human scale. What other kind of place could produce the stark simplicity of a Bedouin tent or a Bushman camp – and also Las Vegas?

## Seascapes

If deserts have only recently become accessible to the average travelling writer, the sea has always been with us, and there is no denying its dramatic power and inspirational qualities for fiction as well as poetry. Some authors such as Joseph Conrad, Nicholas Monserrat and Herman Melville have built their best-known works around it, while others have taken skilful advantage of its metaphorical potential. Moreover, there are some locations about which it is almost impossible to write without the sea playing a major role – Cornwall for example, with Daphne du Maurier setting the pace in *Rebecca*, *Frenchman's Creek* and *Jamaica Inn*.

However it must be said that, while British waters offer some interesting possibilities, the scope widens considerably when you cross that significant, if somewhat grey, stretch of water between Dover and Calais and start thinking of something more exotic. After all, there is the Mediterranean, the Aegean, the Adriatic and the Baltic without going too far afield – not to mention the Atlantic, Pacific, Indian and Arctic Oceans if you are really going places.

A cruise is a good opportunity to renew your acquaintance

with the sea and brush up observation techniques. Maybe you will come up with an original variation on one of the great sea themes such as Ship of Fools, Mutiny on the Bounty and Great Sea Mysteries (Bermuda Triangle, *The Marie-Celeste*, and Who Shot the Cook in the Stern).

The fellow feeling of sea-faring types the world over is legendary, and any writer with even a rudimentary knowlege of fishing or sailing can soon find a boon companion to fill a notebook with stories. But if it is atmosphere and depth of background you want, the sea is amazingly versatile, and exotic seas even more so. Below are just some of the possible ways of using the sea, starting with the more obvious:

- As a symbol of mood swings, restlessness, changeability (weather, winds and tides).
- To suggest undercurrents, dark depths, unknown lurking fears.
- To increase tension and excitement (coming storm, hidden reef, sunken treasure).
- For a sense of vulnerability, of isolation, of being out of one's element.

By no means a seafarer myself, I have nevertheless produced quite a run of short stories featuring the sea. Looking at them again, I can see that it was the *ambivalence* of my own relationship with the sea that was so compelling, and I suspect that this is very common.

As a general rule, it can be helpful to ask yourself why you feel drawn to use certain backgrounds for your work, especially if these involve a particular type of place which is not, so to speak, your natural habitat. With regard to the sea, I reasoned out my own ambivalence as follows:

- Childhood excitement at seeing the sea for the first time in calm, beautiful weather, followed by the loss of several relatives and a close friend in unrelated drowning accidents when in my teens.
- Meeting a retired naval diver when on holiday in Corn-

wall, a brilliant storyteller whose philosophy was as eloquent as it was practical. Always work with the sea, never against it. Take what it gives, but always give it its due.

- Learning to recognise the different types of coastlines and recognising the interaction between land and sea.
- Appreciating that the sea can unite cultures as well as dividing them and that it can promote the spread of ideas and various life forms as well as protecting and isolating.

I am also enthralled by sea myths, in particular that of the mermaid, an ambivalent symbol if ever there was one. Then there is the endless fascination of beachcombing – searching that magic zone that is neither land nor sea for the perfect pebble, a message in a bottle or lost wedding ring. I am quite incurable, to the extent that my idea of perfect holiday happiness would be something wonderfully corny, like having friendly dolphins lead me to a vast sunken treasure, pieces of eight and all. And this is in spite of once being nearly drowned on holiday myself.

All good stuff for the analyst's couch, perhaps, but it is interesting to note that when these little peculiarities of mine surface in short-story form, it is never by the direct route. For instance, in *Sea Change*, there is beautiful Aunt Jennifer, the wife of a favourite ex-sailor uncle. Could she possibly have been the impossible – a mermaid? For *In Search of Paradise*, a girl holidaying in Sri Lanka gets talking to the fiancé of one of the men in the shrimp boats out on the bay. She swaps her expensive gold chain (a present from her married lover) for the other girl's simple shell necklace and resolves at last to leave him. *The Sign of the Dolphin* is about coming to terms with loss. A mother grieving for her beloved adopted daughter, missing one family holiday while swimming with a dolphin. The mother wonders who lured whom, and why afterwards there were always two dolphins in the cove.

## Continents and islands

John Donne's famous proposition that 'No man is an Island, entire of itself; every man is a piece of the Continent, a part of the main', set the tone early for writers to make good metaphorical use for the patterns of land and sea. Just as Gilbert and Sullivan once declared that everyone is born into the world either a Liberal or a Conservative, it could also be said that people divide naturally into those who prefer the freedom of vast, open continental spaces and those who prefer islands because they like to know where the boundaries are.

There is plenty of scope for cheating here, with some people claiming Greenland or even Australia as an island. The main point about an island is that it should feel like one, whatever its size. The term *islomania* has been coined for extreme fascination with islands, and there is even an up-market American travel magazine devoted exclusively to island travel. For British Islanders, the shock of finding themselves on a vast continent, or even pretending to be part of the nearest small one, can be quite disconcerting, especially with our greatest playwright producing wonderful images like 'this gem set in a silver sea'. Real islomanics go for even smaller islands, and should feel at home in the Mediterranean, the Caribbean and the Pacific in particular.

Apart from the psychology of island-versus-continent, islands make wonderfully enclosed little worlds just right for setting up a good story. The success of the TV series *Bergerac* set on Jersey owed much to the same characters being involved week after week in whatever was going on, because that's how islands of that size seem to work. The trick is finding one the right size for your plot. If you can't find one, or don't want to use a real one, you could try making one up. There is more about this in Chapter 10.

Using an island background has the added advantage that it is somehow easier to encapsulate the flavour of the place or to divine its true character. The Durrells, both Lawrence and Gerald, are particularly good at this.

Finally, as a way of drawing together much of what has been said in this chapter, I would recommend the beginning of James Michener's *Hawaii*. The rest of this huge novel I am not so sure about – but there's a writer who didn't sit at the back in geography.

## 7

# WEATHER OR NOT

Most fiction writers when asked if weather is important would nod enthusiastically, remembering perhaps the storm scene in *King Lear*, the searing drought in *The Grapes of Wrath* or the numerous times rain has trickled down the window in sympathy with the heroine's tears. Weather can be used with powerful effect in many ways, and these will be explored. But the note of doubt in this chapter heading is not there simply for the pun. For some types of fiction writing today, making use of the weather can cause more problems than it solves, and this aspect must also be considered.

## Weather and climate

A purist could point out that this chapter is as much about climate as about weather. As a rule of thumb, climate is the meteorological equivalent of a person's general character, including genetic traits and overall behaviour pattern, while weather is more a matter of day-to-day moods within that broader framework. As with people, the writer should make good use of both. They are to some extent interrelated, and the term *weather* is used here to cover both unless a clear distinction is intended.

It has been said that Britain has weather while everywhere else has climate. This admits to a certain meteorological tameness in these parts as well as that infamous changeability. Give or take a hurricane every few centuries, the weather is merely something to grumble about. Even the climate, and

84

we do have one, doesn't run to extremes. Our winters are wimpishly mild, our summers rarely worthy of the name, and sometimes only the state of the vegetation tells us which is which. Indeed some have claimed that it was the British weather which led to the founding of the Empire. Today it is certainly the most common reason for people going abroad for their holidays. All the more reason then, for the writer to follow suit in search of the inspirational and dramatic, backed up of course by the huge amount of information available about weather conditions the world over.

## What to do about the weather

These days this should be considered very carefully before getting too far into a work of any length. Too many beginners ignore it, then get into a pickle. Even experienced writers can get caught out and finish up facing some extensive rewriting. This particularly applies to those with any ambitions to see their work transferred to the screen.

Consider first whether the elements have a real part to play in what you are planning. Most novels and many short stories are enhanced by references to the weather. For TV work, however, writers are often told not to make the storyline dependent on a particular type of weather and to omit references to weather conditions altogether because it causes too many restrictions for the actual filming. Most sit-coms take place in a kind of eternal spring with mid-weight clothing and a marked absence of goose pimples or a sun tan. Scenes are mainly interior, and any outside shooting has to be done in reasonable weather to be consistent. *Alfresco* love scenes are particularly problematic, with actors and actresses full of horror stories about filming in underwear or less on some windswept moor or draughty beach.

'Hollywood rain' has always been something of a joke, even before Gene Kelly famously sang and danced in it. Out come the fire hoses and up go the dry-cleaning bills and make-up costs. Snow to order is even trickier and may involve expensive location shooting which is quite out of the question for many production budgets today.

Anything that is tied to a season, whether it is a heatwave or Christmas, will have to be shot six months to a year in advance. Any story which spans different seasons can also cause problems because shooting has to be extended over such a long time, or else scenes must be faked to give the impression say, of mid-winter, when the sun is in fact cracking the pavements.

Even for a big-budget production like *Out of Africa*, it was interesting to observe that most of the shooting was done in the wet season, which is the off season for tourism and therefore quieter and cheaper. Consequently, everything looked wonderfully lush and green, although the story really hinged on a ruinous drought killing the coffee trees. Writing for TV and films, however, is highly specialised and outside the scope of this book. But anyone hoping to sell screen rights, or wanting to break into this highly competitive field, can learn a lot by studying TV sit-coms, serials and films from this point of view alone.

Radio fiction can be broadly divided into short stories and drama. Short stories for broadcasting don't present any more problems about using weather than any other written fiction. Extra care could perhaps be taken about the language used to describe it so that it sounds right when read aloud. Try reading these two sentences aloud, and you will see the quite different effects they create:

Go for long, lazy, languid vowel sounds for warm, drowsy afternoons.
Take a shot at stinging, brittle, frosty clips if it's an icy night.

You will notice plenty of long Os, As, and also the liquid Ls and Ws in the first one. In the second, short Os and Is predominate and there are lots of Ts, STs and S sounds. (Watch the Ss for radio generally.) There is no need to make a fetish out of it by choosing outlandish words, but a little care can

86

make a subtle difference. The same approach works just as well for other 'noises off', even for work not necessarily designed to be read aloud. A good writer should always be aware of creating sound effects in the reader's mind.

On the other hand, radio drama proper comes with its own set of rules regarding weather. Storms, typhoons, hurricanes, sandstorms, tornadoes, hail and lashing rain are no problem. In fact the BBC have a fine selection of them. But drizzle, frost, snow and fog don't make a sound and a little ingenuity is required if they are necessary to the plot. Tropical heat is easier than a home-grown heat wave because you can at least summon up some cicadas to chirp in the background.

## For, against, or neutral?

If you are not bound by problems associated with filming or drama, you are then free to drum up a storm or in fact any weather conditions at all that could turn the plot or create atmosphere. For the written word, anything goes as long as it's right. Getting it right will come later, but before then, there are other things to consider. For instance, do you see the elements as basically in sympathy with the emotions and tone of your story? Some obvious examples follow:

- the 'tears' of rain mentioned above, or stormy weather of the 'since my man and I ain't together' variety;
- a sudden shaft of sunlight offering illumination or consolation;
- the rainbow, perhaps the oldest of all, suggesting hope and conciliation or even the mythical crook of gold;
- a thundering good tempest to suggest the anger of the gods or lesser mortals.

These and many others have become so clichéd that it is often better to avoid them and try for something more original or subtle.

One technique is to have the weather in direct opposition to mood, acting in counterpoint, as with *Singing in the Rain*. Loss and sadness can be more poignant on a perfect spring morning, first love just as acutely felt in autumn mists as in spring, and a murder twice as nasty on a summer's afternoon than in dark, early-hours drizzle.

Some writers simply describe the weather to set a scene, but take care to choose words which reflect the main character's mood and attitude. It is not what the weather is like that matters so much, but the way it is observed. Raymond Chandler was particularly good at this. The way his laconic private eye, Philip Marlowe, might comment on a bright Californian morning immediately signals that our hero is not exactly the sunny type.

One brilliant example is at the beginning of Robert Harris's thriller *Fatherland*. On a grey, rainy Berlin dawn, the main protagonist, a homicide investigator with the Kriminalpolizei, doesn't turn up his collar in the rain. Instead he tilts his face to it. 'He was a connoisseur of this particular rain. He knew the taste of it, the smell of it. It was Baltic rain, from the north, cold and sea-scented, tangy with salt.' For an instant, he is back twenty years in 'the conning tower of a U-boat, slipping out of Wilhelmshaven, lights doused, into the darkness'. Harris has done so much here. He has immediately given us someone sensitive and observant, alert even at this hour, who has known fear and excitement perhaps too young, and who is probably in for some more right now. What's more, we can feel ourselves warming to this man. And all from some raindrops on an upturned face.

Another technique is to use the elements almost like film theme music, so that a character becomes associated with a particular type of weather. Done discreetly, this can be very effective, but like many devices, once spotted, the effect is weakened. It is also surprising how many writers use weather to set a scene at the beginning of a book and then never mention it again. Perhaps they have their eye on the film rights – or perhaps they've simply forgotten about it.

Before leaving the question of 'for or against', one further point should be noted about the most basic elements of sun and rain. In Britain we tend to regard the sun as a long-lost friend and rain as the enemy. In many tropical areas, the reverse is true. Rain is something to be prayed for, worshipped, and danced in when it comes, while the sun is to be avoided. The 'mad dogs and Englishmen' scene is still very much with us, but with skin cancer and global warming, even the English are having to revise their attitudes to the sun. And as for being 'too much in the sun', remember the despairing wail of Kenya's Happy Valley set in *White Mischief*: 'Oh God, not *another* bloody beautiful morning!'

## The atmosphere

Most writers know instinctively that creating the right atmosphere is extremely important, and that the weather can play a useful, sometimes crucial, part in this. But when it comes to getting the best out of the weather in this respect, it is very helpful to know a little about *the* atmosphere itself – the gaseous layer that surrounds the Earth in which all our weather takes place.

Everyone knows that the earth is coldest at the poles and warmest within the tropics. But while temperature, seasonality and rainfall are important, and will be dealt with later, basic weather *patterns* are often a blank. For the writer this could mean missing out on potentially useful background material.

It doesn't matter where you are in the world, the basic weather patterns are determined mainly by whether a place is experiencing low atmospheric pressure, high atmospheric pressure, or in the battle zone between the two. Each has its own special features, and for the writer in search of an appropriate metaphor, or seeking to organise some interesting weather to move along the plot, it is helpful to know something about them.

First let us clear up the small matter of high and low atmospheric pressure. For pressure here, read weight. Air can be weighed and the instrument that does this is a barometer, which is no more than a refined weighing scale. A lot of air pressing down on the surface will give a high reading – hence high pressure. So it is sinking air that causes high pressure.

Conversely, light, lifting air, air that is rising, will not weigh heavily on the barometer. It gives a low barometric reading – hence low pressure. Whether the air is rising or sinking (or in meteorological terms, if the pressure is low or high) is very important indeed because it determines not just the weather, but also the health and behaviour of the people living under it.

## High-pressure conditions

An area of high pressure is where the air is sinking. The term high pressure simply refers to the high reading it gives on a barometer as it presses down on it. The following characteristics are associated with high-pressure areas, and as you check through you might like to be thinking how a writer could use them.

- Generally stable conditions sometimes lasting for weeks.
- Rain is very unlikely. Wild, wet, windy weather is right out.
- Generally clear skies, so that the days are bright and sunny and the stars are visible at night.
- Because of rapid night cooling of the surface, dew is common, and in colder places this shows as frost.
- In damp areas, mist, ground fog or 'heat haze' is common in the early mornings, burning off as the day progresses.
- The air may feel dry and crackly with static, especially inland. Dust, pollen and pollution become trapped by the stable, sinking air, and in cities, 'smog' and photochemical fog can be a problem.

It comes as no surprise that it is the presence of a large high pressure cell over the Mediterranean in the summer months that causes the kind of conditions sun-starved Northern Europeans crave, and the same goes for California and a few other favoured places such as the Cape area of South Africa and Southern Australia. When Britain gets a heatwave, it is usually because the edge of a high-pressure cell has somehow drifted up our way. Most of the time Britain's weather is dominated by low pressure, which is a different thing altogether.

In short, with high pressure, the atmospheric conditions may be stable, but people are not. Tempers shorten; migraines, violence, hay fever and chest problems increase; and it is even blamed for the onset of certain types of madness. The New York Police Department dreads a summer high-pressure spell, but in Los Angeles, they have this condition most of the time.

High-pressure conditions certainly have their uses, especially for psychological thrillers or crime novels where an edgy or violent atmosphere is required. Morning mist or fog can also be very handy. The ultimate in fog as a metaphor is probably that famous beginning of Dickens's *Bleak House*. Romantic writers on the other hand will appreciate the sultry afternoons, calm, moonlit waters and starry nights of a typical Mediterranean 'high'.

## Low-pressure conditions

In an area of low pressure, the air is light and lifting. The result is atmospheric instability. Chances of rain increase dramatically, because the air has only to lift far enough into the cooler upper layers of the atmosphere for clouds to form, possibly producing rain. Strangely enough, low pressure is usually better for human health and behaviour than high pressure, with a few notable exceptions, as we shall see.

But there is much more to low pressure than a good shower to relieve the tension. Even more than high pressure, 'lows' are the writer's friend, largely because they take so many forms. In fact there is a whole family of low-pressure cells, from enormous tropical ones that sit over half a continent and cause an entire wet season, through to our own 'Atlantic depressions', and right down to the whirling 'dust devils' that zig-zag around deserts or hot city streets. Incidentally, note the confusing terms 'depressions' and 'lows'. It is only the barometer reading that is depressed or low. The air itself is lifting.

The main thing about low-pressure areas (or the cyclone family as they are known in the trade) is that whatever their size they act as a vortex, drawing in air to compensate for all the lifting – a useful metaphor, perhaps. However, the world being what it is, i.e. round and spinning, these winds do not come in straight, but become deflected, hence the swirling patterns which can be seen on every satellite picture and weather chart.

If it is turbulence you are after, these are the zones of turbulence *par excellence*. The middle, or 'eye', of these systems tends to be the quietest, although it is often humid and rain is still a strong possibility. But it is on the outside edges (called fronts) of these systems that the real action takes place. The size of the system and how much difference there is between the low pressure inside and the relatively higher pressure round it determine how violent this action will be and what forms it will take. What is more, these systems move around on 'tracks' that are not always as regular as they might be. When all this combines, the cyclone family is capable of producing some real football hooligans in the world of weather.

Terry Pratchett exploits this concept in *Wyrd Sisters*, one of his very successful Discworld fantasy series. He sees a storm as a 'bit part' actor rather than a mere backdrop: 'This was its big chance. It had spent years hanging around the provinces putting in some useful work as a squall, building up experience, making contacts, leaping out on unsuspecting shepherds or blasting quite small oak trees. Now an opening in the weather had given it an opportunity to strut its hour, and it was building up its role in the hope of being spotted by one of the major climates.'

Atlantic depressions are the dozy cousins of the family, but even they have their moments. They can also make forecasting very difficult and the weatherman always gets the blame. Some of the best known special effects produced by members of the cyclone family on the move are listed below:

- The barometer falls (i.e. the readings drop) as the system approaches. A very sharp drop in pressure can be detected even by some birds and animals, who will instinctively seek shelter. The wind gets up, clouds appear and rain is very likely to follow.
- The rain can be anything from a few spots to a cloudburst, while the wind might even be hurricane force.
- There may be a lull ('the eye') if you happen to be underneath the middle, after which the other front passes over with a repeat performance.
- Thunder, lightning and hail can occur in frontal areas, and blizzards if it is cold enough for snow instead of rain.
- Twisters, tornados and dust-devils are land-based violent 'lows' and may produce dry electrical storms rather than rain, while hurricanes, typhoons, water spouts and tropical cyclones pick up much moisture over warm seas and then swing in over the land.
- Maximum instability in the weather will always be found when a 'low' is near the sea or mountains, and particularly in tropical areas.
- Eventually the system will 'blow itself out', which means that the pressure has now evened out. This expression is also used incorrectly to mean that the whole thing has moved elsewhere.

There is no shortage of plot potential or metaphorical content here – dramatic, even melodramatic, erotic, fantastical, comic. The volatile cyclone family can come up with all kinds of surprises if you let your imagination wander a little.

## A word about wind

It is the difference between high and low pressure on a world
scale that is responsible for the great wind belts. Always
blowing from high to low pressure, these winds are known
for their persistence and regularity – the Westerlies, the
North-east and South-east Trade winds, the Roaring Forties,
various monsoon winds and so on. A wind is named after the
direction from which it comes, because that is much more
significant in determining its character than where it is going.

Some areas of the world (the British Isles is one) stay more
or less within the same wind belt most of the year, but in
others there is a sharp change of direction according to season which can effect many aspects of living there. One novel
at least, called, appropriately enough, *Wind*, by James Her-
bert, has a plot entirely based on the idea that the whole
world is afflicted by a mighty wind. While this is of course a
meteorological impossibility, it works if disbelief can be suf-
ficiently suspended, rather as with Noah and the Flood. *Gone
with the Wind* hardly needs mentioning for its neat use of
metaphor, as a whole way of life is swept away. But it is
always worth remembering that the author nearly blew it
(pardon the appalling pun). She wanted to call it *Bye Bye
Black Sheep*.

Local winds are also worth investigating, two of the best
known being the Sirocco and the Mistral.

The **Sirocco** is a southerly wind affecting the North African
coast. Blowing as it does from the Sahara, it is hot, dusty and
dry. It is rarest in summer and most frequent and devastating
in spring, when it can wither olive and vine blossoms. On
crossing the Mediterranean to reach Sicily or Southern Italy,
it picks up moisture and becomes enervatingly humid.
Known as the Khamsin in Egypt, the Levache in Southern
Spain, the Chilii in Tunisia and Gibli in Libya, it is often held
responsible for violent temper and irrational behaviour. Fortunately it usually only lasts a day or two.

The **Mistral** is another unwelcome visitor – a cold north-
erly or north-westerly wind which funnels down the Rhone

valley from the colder Alpine areas. It is particularly bad in winter and early spring. Rightly maligned in *A Year in Provence*, it is responsible for distinctive tree windbreaks round crops and the thick-walled traditional houses being windowless on the Mistral side. Skies are clear, but local tales of the Mistral's damage potential are not always exaggerations. Its Italian cousin, the Tramontano, does much the same for the Plain of Lombardy, and the Iberian version, the Tramontana, hailing from the Pyrenees, is no more welcome in Spain.

Not all local winds are complete villains. The Fohn wind from some high mountain areas warms as it descends, causing a thaw and acting as the herald of spring. In North America it is called the Chinook and there is a lovely description of its effects in *Little House on the Prairie*. The desperate family, snow-bound in a log cabin, hears strange creaking and thuds one night and realises that the worst is over. The warm Chinook has arrived, stealthy as an Indian, and huge icicles are toppling from the roof. It is that kind of observation which makes work come alive.

Similarly, the sudden splitting of furniture and ominous creaking of roof timbers at night often announces the arrival of the Harmattan wind in West Africa. This dry-season wind from the desert is known as the Doctor if it reaches the normally humid coast because it dries up various infections. Nearer its desert source, this wind can sandpaper eyeballs to a fiery pink and have lettuce wilting on your plate as you watch.

Wind as devil and destroyer, harbinger, healer, means of transport, sneaky breeze or wrath of God – the choice is yours. As with anything else, the secret lies in researching it properly and using it aptly and with originality to make your readers feel they are there.

# 8

# FLORA AND FAUNA

Plant and animal life are less likely to be crucial in a work of fiction than the human factor, landscape or the weather. However, such things as unfamiliar trees and flowers, strange bird song and so on, can help enormously to bring a place alive, create a mood or illuminate a character's feelings. Without them, readers will surely feel short-changed. It would be a pity then, not to exploit these fully merely through a lack of knowledge or confidence.

## Observation and identification

In a heroic attempt to get the young to look at worms and beetles without squealing, Lord Baden-Powell stoutly declared that anything is beautiful if you look at it closely enough. Botanists and zoologists would certainly agree that minute observation is the key to identification. The busy writer, however, doesn't always have the time or the background to approach things scientifically, while enthusiasts in one field can easily become quite lost in another.

In Britain we are lucky in that generations of keen naturalists and gardeners have produced a mass of accessible information on our native and naturalised wild life, much of it beautifully illustrated. The opposite is true of books for the non-specialist on exotic flora and fauna, and it can be very frustrating to have the interest, but be stumped by a general lack of suitable information. Below are some suggestions for self-help in this direction:

- Look for simple, colour-illustrated books or magazine features on house plants, many of which are dwarfed or juvenile versions of exotic cousins. Hibiscus, bougainvillea, oleander, poinsettia, morning glory and a host of others will soon become familiar friends if you can keep house-plant illustrations of them with you.
- Visit a good nursery, plant collection, or botanical garden. The plants are usually labelled, with a note on their area of origin, range, history and uses. Some collections are highly specialised according to area or type of plant – palms, cacti, New World, Oriental, marsh, alpines, orchids, medicinals and so on, which is useful if you have somewhere or something specific in mind.
- Read novels rather than guide books about the area, because generally speaking guide books don't bother with plant life, while many good novelists do. Make a note of any plants mentioned that interest you and try to identify them when on the spot.
- Ask your tour guide or the local people what things are called. They may not know, but can often come up with a local name which sounds great by itself or translates into something poetic, funny, or even endearingly rude. This is a good ice-breaker, and could prompt someone knowledgeable in the group to come to your rescue. My favourite on-location name is for skinks, those agile little lizards that whizz across polished floors as if jet-propelled. It was produced after much thought by a small African boy and probably gains in the translation. Apparently his people called them 'tomorrow-is-too-late'.

Sometimes identification is not actually necessary. Such matters are best taken at the pace of your protagonists, and should always be in keeping with the tone of the book. In William Boyd's *Brazzaville Beach*, for example, there is a lot of expert detail about plant life, but the heroine is a naturalist working in a West African chimpanzee reserve, so that is exactly how she would relate to her surroundings. Another type of protagonist, say a London detective seconded somewhere very far from his home patch to investigate a British tourist's murder, might crash his way uncomfortably and indiscriminately through bush savanna and mangrove swamp. The unfamiliarity of it all would be the keynote. He might then be allowed the odd acute observation on the size of some thorns that slowed him down, or how it feels to be surrounded by the noises of the bush when you haven't a clue what's making them. Having said that, it is generally a wise precaution to know exactly what you are writing about. If appropriate, your protagonist can then 'get it wrong' in style.

In the interests of getting it right, Fig. 2 shows some of the more common 'holiday' plants, tabulated according to the vexed question of whether they smell or not. Many people, even writers, assume that just because a flower looks good it must have a scent. With tropical blossom it is more often the smaller, inconspicuous ones that have a strong scent. The gaudy types don't need it – the insects find them anyway. The table is backed up by the note-type material below which could be used as a starter for your own notebook.

**For your notebook**

*Flamboyant(e),* Poinciana regia

aka, Flame of the Forest or Flame Tree. (This last name is confusing because there is another Flame Tree which is actually the African Tulip Tree, see below.) A native of Madagascar, but followed colonialism round the tropics. A truly lovely tree in every way, not a forest giant, but spreading like a feathery umbrella to provide shade and colour in gardens and main thoroughfares. Flowers exceptionally showy (see chart). Leaves fern-like, a baby-pea green. Bark silver-grey, smooth. Trunk rarely straight, branches flat and spreading (imagine a leopard lying along one). Spectacular hard black pods like boomerangs, often

## SCENTED AND NON-SCENTED

| NO SCENT | DEFINITE SCENT |
|---|---|
| Bougainvillea – purple/puce/ scarlet thorny climbers found round tourist hotels anywhere warmer than UK. | Moonflower – like bindweed on steroids. Only opens white trumpets at night. Pure opium. |
| Flamboyant – massive orange/ scarlet sprays of orchid-like flowers, ferny leaves, huge long black pods. | Frangipani – Hawaiian greeting garlands made out of these. Like cheap sun-tan oil. |
| Oleander – straggly bush with olivy leaves and pink/white small rose-type flowers | Wild garlic – horrendous. Don't be tempted by coy lily-of-the-valley looks. |
| Hibiscus – flaring red/pink trumpet flowers with prominent polleny spike on stocky bushes. | Jasmine (tropical) – small white flowers, very sweet and cloying. What most temples smell of. |
| Jacaranda – distinctive soft lilac shade: spindly tree with ferny leaves. | Citrus – orange, lemon. Flowers like jasmine. Leaves also good. |
| Morning glory – convolvulus creeper with showy indigo trumpet flowers. | Coffee – small white waxy flowers sweet like citrus and jasmine. |
| Cassia – bold yellow sprays like a heavyweight laburnum on a tropical hardwood. Lacks finesse. | Many Mediterranean and semi-desert shrubs with tough tiny leaves smell strongly – rosemary lavender, various eucalypti, etc. If in doubt, tweak. |

Figure 2.

exceeding 60 cm/2 ft in length – worth bringing home – rattles with attractive stone-mottled seeds. Always flowers at the time of greatest heat, usually just before the rainy season.

*African Tulip Tree,* Spathodea campanulata

aka Flame Tree especially in East Africa, as in *The Flame Trees of Thika*. A native of the forest fringes, found all over tropical Africa and often planted near habitation. Large bright orange/scarlet overblown-tulip flowers with yellow edges grow stiffly in 2/3s at ends of the branches, often too high to reach. A crude looker compared to the above. Coarse, curled, darkish leaves divided into pairs of leaflets, like an ash but much larger. 15 cm/6 in pod containing winged seeds.

*Crown of Thorns,* Euphorbia millii

You know it when you see it because the name sounds so right. But it definitely wasn't Christ's crown of thorns. Although now found near human habitation round the Mediterranean and similar areas, it is a native of Madagascar. Low, creeping bush consisting almost entirely of long vicious thorns packed closely on grey-brown branches. Leaves are tiny, sparse and dark green. Little red-bracted flowers give the appearance of blood-drops. Sap weepy and poisonous. Often grown to keep goats/thieves out.

*Teak Tree,* Tectona grandis

Easily recognised by huge leaves that look like brown paper wrappings when they fall. Pale papery bark with dense oily orange wood. Large panicles of daisy-sized greeny white flowers. Fruit like a tiny fig. Often grown in plantations in African and Eastern tropics, for railways sleepers, heavy construction and marine use (rot and ant resistant). Also as a shade tree or windbreak along roads. Native of South-east Asia. Felling of natural teak forest now forbidden in Thailand, thereby leaving many furniture makers and elephants unemployed. Scent? Looks like it could be pollinated by bats or moths. Check.

With the range of holiday destinations widening every year, you will soon have your own favourites – baobabs in the Gambia, giant agarves in Mexico, Californian redwoods, coconut palms, Indian banyan trees – and be making new discoveries all the time. But be warned, as with almost everything, those precious details that add authenticity and flavour soon become a blur. Select your targets and take proper notes, even about the bits you think you might not need – bark texture, flowering times, uses, leaf fall, and which birds or insects are frequent visitors. Get a picture if you can, your own or bought. I am constantly surprised at which tiny details I actually use, and what I missed and wish I hadn't. But then it's too late.

For general use, keep an old unused diary or large calendar, and mark budding/flowering/fruiting times etc for useful plants by blocking off relevant weeks. *First snowdrop, horse chestnuts out, bananas ripe in Jamaica, olive harvest (Tunisia)*, etc. Use to make yearly comparisons, or with times elsewhere. Remember, even Jane Austen got it wrong. She had apple trees flowering in June, and that was in her own back yard.

## It's a jungle out there

Or is it? Apart from the individual plants, there is also the question of the way plants occur naturally in particular association with each other, and then the names by which these *plant associations* are known. A plant association includes everything from trees right down to the smallest lichens and fungi which have evolved by living together over a long time under particular conditions. Some plant associations are well known, like rain forest, tundra, coniferous forest, savanna and so on, while others have more technical names used mainly by botanists. What is more, each area has its own none-too-scientific ideas about what to call its great outdoors. Using the wrong name is a sure sign of a greenhorn, whether traveller or writer.

There are so many variations that listing them would be complicated and tedious, but the word 'jungle' is a case in point. It is derived from a Sanskrit word meaning, of all things, a desert or wasteland. It then came to mean any waste ground, and as this was always overgrown in the more humid areas of India, it took on its more familiar meaning – dense thickets with a tangle of undergrowth. The term should not be used for true rain forest, but only for where clearance or waterways have let in light for undergrowth development. The term is used most frequently in South-east Asia where it originated, and where much of the original forest has given way to a degraded tangle of bamboo, understorey plants and creepers. It is occasionally used in South America.

Where it is almost never used is Africa. Here the term 'bush' covers everything that isn't semi-desert or tall forest. 'Veldt' is used only in Southern Africa for mainly grassy areas, but as the word comes from Dutch/Afrikaans, it doesn't travel well. For Australia, 'outback' serves much the same purpose as 'bush', but there are many variations, especially in the better wooded areas.

Similarly, there are local names for different types of Mediterranean scrub, the best known being *maquis*, with California having its own variations on the theme – sage brush, *chaparral*, etc. Read it up and ask around.

## Crop plants

In most holiday destinations, you won't always be face to face with thousands of square miles of untamed wilderness. So much of the original vegetation has gone, and in the Mediterranean in particular it is hard to imagine Classical times when most of it was forested with various types of oak, pine, sweet chestnut and cedar. Except in extensive mountain areas like the Taurus of Turkey or the Moroccan Rif, what is left is mostly scrub or farmland. So prominent is the role of farming in many landscapes that it is worth looking at crops in their own right. There are two ways of doing this – at the crop itself, and then at the way it affects the landscape.

Thanks to refrigeration, increased standards of living and multi-cultural cookery, most people are now familiar with a great variety of exotic fruit and vegetables. Fresh yams, sweet potatoes, paw-paw, sugar cane, mangoes, cassava, okra, ginger, limes – all these and more can now be bought in Britain. It is a start, but recognising the parent plant growing on location may not be so simple. It certainly wasn't for one sophisticated and intelligent New Yorker I knew, who was very surprised to find that cauliflowers do not come from a tree.

Sometimes identification is easy: if it is the Far East and growing in small flooded fields, it must be rice, and so on. Many tours will often include a trip to a typical farm or plantation and it is always much more interesting than it sounds. There are demonstrations of all kinds, often using traditional methods – olive-pressing, tea-picking, rubber-tapping, tobacco-curing – and tastings of everything from wine and Camembert to Blue Mountain coffee or coconut milk. It is a good way to get the smell and texture of the produce and gives a sense of it in context.

Just as interesting to the writer is the way in which farming affects the landscape. For example, olive trees are one of the most welcome and familiar holiday sights, with the silvery sheen on the foliage undersides and the characteristic gnarling of the trunks. Yet the manner of the cultivation differs from place to place and can greatly affect the scenery. On the European shores of the Mediterranean, olive groves tend to be open, smallish and informal. They are often terraced, or create a patchwork with vineyards or dark leaved citrus groves, while sheep graze beneath. On the North African side, the effect is much more stark. Mile upon mile of absolutely regimented rows grow in bare red ground or bleached sand, stretching to the horizon with hardly a wisp of dry grass or a straggly weed to relieve the austere scene.

Rice-growing creates one of the world's most fascinating manmade landscapes, with places like the Philippines and

Indonesia ahead even of China in the amazing terraced hillsides produced by the toil of generations. By complete contrast the *shambas* of East Africa, family plots growing a mixture of bananas, maize, cassava and vegetables, seem delightfully haphazard. Apart from an odd ridge for maize or groundnuts, there is not a straight line to be seen. The ground is never completely cleared and things seem to grow in a random, friendly jumble. It is not random of course. Beans or yam vines climb up maize or guinea corn stalks, the wide-leaved bananas, plantains and cocoyams shelter the bitter-leaf, okra and peppers beneath, while melons and calabash vines (gourds) for pots are trained over the thatched roofs out of the way of ants.

Tea, coffee, rubber, sisal, cotton, oil palm and many more all produce distinctive scenery. Sometimes the result clashes with the environment and local lifestyles, but elsewhere the effect is of harmony, even beauty. Livestock grazing produces a variety of pasture patterns, while marsh reclamation and desert irrigation can change a place beyond recognition for good or ill. For the writer, places that are a disaster waiting to happen can be intriguing – perhaps through drought, flood risk, bad land management, over-population or greed. *Feeling* carefully around what you see will give your work that extra edge or resonance and could spark off new lines of thought.

### Animals in fiction

With animals, especially the larger exotic ones, identification is not usually the problem. It is more a matter of acute observation and deciding how to use the wild life effectively. There are four main ways in which the animal kingdom can be of use in fiction:

1. As an integral part of the plot, where the animal is itself the hero of the story, as in *Black Beauty, Tarka the Otter*

et cetera, or where the hopes and dreams of the main protagonist are tied intimately to the fate of an individual animal or group – *Brazzaville Beach*, *Androcles and the Lion*, *Moby Dick*. Animals can also be very handy as murder weapons (poisonous snakes and spiders) or for disposing of the evidence (crocodiles, sharks, ants, et cetera).

2. As a working background – where veterinary, stable, zoo, conservation or other work involves close contact with animals – Jilly Cooper's *Riders*, *Jaws*, most of Dick Francis and a host of teen and sub-teen books.

3. To add atmosphere and colour, enhance the mood or provide interesting forms of transport as required (camels, elephants, horse-drawn carriages or sledges, gallops along the shore, et cetera). Bird calls and insect noises are particularly evocative, see the next heading.

4. For allegory, fantasy or magical realism at any level from *Little Red Riding Hood* to *The Company of Wolves*. Here the same animals often crop up in widely different cultures. Snakes and crocodiles, rabbits and hares, foxes, and wolves of course, seem to reflect certain aspects of the human psyche that writers have exploited to great effect since the Old Testament was at the first draft stage.

5. To show something about the protagonists themselves. How someone reacts to animals is extremely revealing. I know one author who has to decide first whether her characters are cat or dog lovers before she can go any further. Some people are affected by sheer bulk even if the creature is harmless, while others hate anything that flaps or buzzes, however small. Some want desperately to communicate with animals, while others seek only to admire from a distance. Some need to dominate or destroy and others again to mother or anthropomorphise.

Naturally, you will want to get close without taking risks. Don't be tempted by dogs in Third World countries, however dozy they seem. They may not appreciate it, and rabies injections are very unpleasant. The same goes for monkeys, chimpanzees and bears on chains. Apart from the risk of a bite, these are kept in cruel conditions, and no one who cares for animals would want to encourage their owners or the dealers. Unless you disapprove of all forms of animal captivity, however, there are many kinds of farms, ranches, training centres, reserves and aquaria for creatures as diverse as snakes, crocodiles, butterflies, ostriches, pearl oysters, elephants and killer whales.

If you are invited, don't miss the chance to tickle a dolphin, stroke a python or peer into an elephant's trunk. In the interests of fiction I have had a red-kneed tarantula the size of a saucer walking over my fingers, and learned that riding on an elephant's head is murder in shorts because the animal is covered in bristly hairs you would never normally see. But there is something about actually feeling behind an elephant's ears with your bare feet to guide it that brings emotions you didn't know you had straight to the surface. For other people, ten minutes' ride on a camel and they are in a fantasy world of their own.

Exaggerating animal size, strength or aggressive tendencies is rather old hat, and the Guinness Book of Records will put you right on the longest, highest, heaviest – in spite of what the locals may claim. That is not to say there isn't still a place for plague-and-swarm fiction of the *Day of the Killer Bees* variety, but this is really a branch of the science-fiction and fantasy genres. The tendency is now generally away from anthropomorphism and sentimentality at one extreme and *Boys' Own Paper*/Hemingway adventure at the other. The middle ground emphasises themes of co-operation and understanding where animals are concerned. Occasionally over-the-top emotions and mysticism still creep in. Treating the animal kingdom truthfully is the least a writer can do.

**Animal noises off**

However you choose to incorporate the wild life in your work, you will have to provide the sound effects for your readers. The range of sounds made by the animal kingdom is enormous, and there is certainly no shortage of terms. But again, beware of clichés. One editor is on record as saying that he instantly bins any script containing the words 'Somewhere a dog barked'.

But dogs do bark. They also growl, snarl, yelp, whine, whimper, sigh, bay, howl, scratch, sniff and pant. Lions roar, donkeys bray, cocks crow and ducks quack – and it doesn't matter where you are in the world, the sound is more or less the same. Sometimes it is less intrusive simply to leave it at that, in the same way that there may be a hundred variations on 'he said', but in the end, 'he said' may be all that is required.

For the real expert, however, more or less the same might not be good enough. Numerous studies have shown that regional accents for animals, birds and insects definitely exist. Whales off California do not have quite the same song patterns as their Australian cousins. The language of the great apes varies from one region to another, and some types of birds in Britain have local accents. An interesting snippet perhaps – the sort of thing that the fiction writer collects like a magpie or hoards like a squirrel (to air some more animal clichés). But unless material like this is used skilfully in fiction, it becomes just another example of what one editor calls *So-what-ery*.

For getting unfamiliar animal noises right, there is nothing better than having a cassette recorder handy so that you can mull over it back home. Wild life documentaries are also a wonderful source of exotic sound effects, from zebras bronking (my word – I just can't think of another that works better) to bull frogs in the reeds. And at least you don't get the flies.

While there is no doubt that animal noises can be very useful, their absence may be just as effective. Remember George Bernard Shaw's put-down of South Africa as a place where the birds had no song, the flowers no perfume, the men no manners and the women no morals. Perhaps the most famous case of animal absentee-ism is in Sherlock Holmes, with the dog that didn't bark.

## Titles that come naturally

To round off on an inspirational note – while researching this chapter, I was struck by how many works of fiction, irrespective of length or genre, use flora and fauna in the title. Some are famous enough to need no introduction – *The Thorn Birds*, *The Day of the Jackal*, *Eye of the Tiger*, *The Grapes of Wrath* and so on. The use is often figurative or metaphorical, and the best have a rhythmic quality that is both evocative and satisfying.

Short stories writers too, often lean towards the natural world for their themes or titles. Some classics include *Pigeon Feathers* (John Updike), *The Fever Trees* (Ruth Rendell), *The Fly* (Katherine Mansfield), *Odour of Chrysanthemums* (D. H. Lawrence) and *The Camberwell Beauty* (V. S. Pritchett). There is no copyright in titles, but as a general rule, it is better to check library catalogues for what you have in mind. The work may in fact be long out of print, so note the date and the publisher. Checking is particularly important if the key word is vital to the book, and the final decision as to whether a change is necessary can be left to your agent/editor/publisher.

## 9

# THE ART OF SELECTION

Much of what has gone before was about preparation for writing rather than writing itself. A lot of it could just as easily apply to producing travel articles as well as fiction. There are of course some writers who are successful in both fields – indeed it is these very people who are most aware of the differences between the two. It is in the selecting of what you need from all the preparation that the differences really begin to show. Most important of all is how you use your material.

## Fiction versus features

'Very nice/interesting/humorous, but it reads like a feature/ essay.' Almost everyone who has ever written a short story must have heard that criticism at least once. Such remarks tend to crop up more often when the work is set abroad, and there are a number of reasons for this. The first is to do with subject matter and the other two are more related to style.

### 1. 'But it really happened that way'

A common enough cry, with abroad being the most likely place where adventures or events out of the ordinary happen these days. The temptation is then to write it up as a story more or less as it happened. This almost never works, even when told in third person rather than first and minor details are changed. The reasons for this are quite complex, and of course apply equally to work set at home. Usually it comes down to two things. The first is that real life is messy, long-winded and often lacks both structure and meaning which the writer then has to impose. The second is that the writer has not yet acquired the necessary distancing from the real events to deal with the first effectively. So if you are itching to turn something that actually happened into a short story, block-buster, or whatever, do take another look at it. If in doubt, seek advice from books on general fiction which deal with this problem more fully.

### 2. Clogging the works

This problem dogs historical novelists in particular, but occurs in any fiction where background research is important. Too much material is included that either swamps the story-line or is simply irrelevant or inappropriate. It's a case of 'I've found this out, and I'm not going to waste it.' For some editors, slowing down the story is the worst offence possible these days, and there is nothing like too much detail, however fascinating, for doing just that.

### 3. Sounding like a guide book

In using even relevant background or atmospheric detail, the writer unconsciously imitates the guide-book style, so that the effect is somehow stilted, clichéd, journalistic or academic. One magazine fiction editor dreads stories set abroad because so many sound as if the writer has 'swallowed a guide book'. Newspaper travel editors say the same, so obviously beginner feature writers too, are not immune to this stylistic fault.

But what separates fiction more than anything else from

factual writing is the presence of some kind of plot. Something has already been said about the role of location in this respect in Chapter 1. What we are concerned with now is making sure the right story happens in the right place.

## Plot and location

To recap briefly on the relationship between plot and location – at the two extremes we have:

1. The transplanted story, where you already have a basic storyline or theme and are looking for a suitable place to set it.
2. The location-based story, where the story grows directly from an already chosen location.

Both have their strong and weak points. A storyline or theme that transplants easily is likely to have almost by definition a wide, even universal, appeal. There may be a large number of possible places where it could happen, and simply by changing a few names and using atmospheric detail skilfully, you could come up with an interesting, saleable story.

If transplanting a story is what you have in mind, then a check through the following should maximise your chances of finding the right place in which to set it.

- Have you been adventurous or imaginative enough in choosing a location? See Chapter 2.
- Bear in mind not just your own travel experiences but those of your characters. Senior citizens are just as likely to be found in exotic locations these days as the young, who more often frequent the cheaper destinations, and ferry, bus and train stations more than airports.
- Make sure you highlight particular aspects of a place that in some way enhance the atmosphere, reflect something about the characters or add a unique edge to it.

- Remember the 'It happened in Marrakesh, but it might as well have been Margate' trap.
- Don't let the location suddenly get out of hand and swamp either the storyline or the emotional content.

If on the other hand you are in some way tied to a particular location, and are in need of a plot, then a different approach is required. Letting the story grow from a place may seem like a more satisfying option than the above. It has an organic feel to it. But don't be deceived – getting it right is hard work.

For location-based plots, simply being there and hoping one will drop into your lap like a ripe coconut is not enough, as the preceding chapters have been at pains to point out. You might be lucky, but why take the risk? Do your preparation thoroughly and get a good framework in place upon which to hang anything new that comes along. The more you can tie in, the better your chances of coming up with something that works. Many attempts have been made to analyse the creative process, but for me, what happens most is that two things suddenly connect. More than that, they seem to overlay each other and fuse. The more you know, the more chance of collisions, connections, overlayings, fusings – or whatever the process is for you.

Don't despair if nothing strikes by the time you have to leave. Many good stories have been written in retrospect, long after the writer has almost given up. Take comfort from one of my favourite definitions: Education is what is left after the facts have been forgotten. A good story can be like that too. These common images for fiction contain similar notions:

- cream rising to the surface;
- clear consommé – the refined essence from the meat and bones;
- a diamond cut perfectly to reflect maximum light;
- the tip of the iceberg.

Note in each case the element of a residue to be discarded,

or of something unseen below. In fact it is what you take away or cannot see that makes the finished product what it is.

## Birth of a story

Having looked briefly at the two extremes of the story/location relationship, most people may find that they operate somewhere between the two. It is like knowing where the edges of the swimming pool are so that you can thrash around confidently in the middle.

To illustrate, here is an example: I was going on holiday to Crete, for no better reason than that I hadn't been before and it sounded interesting. So I had my location – but whereabouts in Crete? The coastal resorts (beach or harbour), the mountains (by all accounts quite spectacular) the archaeological sites (famous or not so)? Suddenly Crete seemed an awfully big place.

Naturally I wanted a storyline. But to some extent this was already dictated by the needs of the particular magazine I was aiming at. It had to be relationship-based (but not a starry-eyed first romance) probably with a woman of the magazine's target age as the main protagonist.

While reading up on Crete, I noticed a place called the Samaria Gorge. It had only recently opened up to mainstream tourism and its main attractions were the views, rare plants and clouds of butterflies. Then I spotted a newspaper travel article about it. The writer maintained that blisters and twisted ankles were a feature of the day-long hike, together with a feeling of camaraderie, not to say relief, at having completed the precipitous ten-mile slog at all. Now that had some potential, which I jotted down as follows:

- Who would do a trip like this and why? Interest (walking, butterflies)? Need to escape – from what or whom?
- Plenty of scope for accidents and problems here. Whose accident?
- In a partnership or single – better single (more vulnerability, need to rely on others)?

- Why single? Newly single? Why?

Perhaps it was the travel writer mentioning a part of the gorge called the Iron Gates – a constriction no wider than an arm span, beyond which was the first glimpse of the sea – that made me think along the lines of an emotional recuperation/light-at-the-end-of-the-tunnel story. So even before I landed, I had a theme in mind and some lovely imagery to compliment it. The result was 'Love is like a Butterfly' which sold to *Family Circle* and abroad. And it was the nice butterfly man who twisted his ankle, not our heroine . . .

## When it's got to go, it's got to go

A famous film director, when asked what he wanted written on his gravestone, replied, 'Cut!' Not wanting to think quite that far ahead, I have that word pinned on the board above my word processor. Before you put pen to paper or fingers to keys is the best time to remind yourself just how ruthless and manipulative you will have to be when it comes to choosing what goes and what stays. This might hurt, but it's better to get used to the idea now rather than later. Promise yourself to watch out for these four villains in particular and avoid them from the start.

1. Any nice bits of atmosphere that are not used in some way to contribute either to the emotional tone of the story, to our understanding of the characters, or to the plot.
2. Fascinating facts of local history, geography, archaeology, et cetera or indeed anything at all irrelevant to your story.
3. Longish purely descriptive passages, however well written or relevant. It's a sad fact, but the average reader's attention span is less than it was. Even Dickens wouldn't get away with some of his longer passages now because often such description is no longer necessary. People travel more, and television and cinema have done much to fill in the gaps.
4. Guide-book or academic phraseology. Yes, that again.

The more thorough the homework, the greater the danger that chunks of your block-buster will sound like someone's PhD trying to get out. Here, it is not the type of detail or the amount, but whether the language used is right for the tone of your story.

Having set up the principles, the next problem is applying them. Exactly *how* can that valuable material you have spent so long internalising (not learning, it isn't the same) be used effectively in your work? It is very difficult to offer general advice here because each story is so individual. Perhaps the most helpful thing is to take some of this raw stuff of research and then see how it can be used in different circumstances.

For this, I have cheated a little. First, I found a brilliant example from a well-known novel of a place being used to maximum possible effect. It is the second passage below, from Chapter 1 of *A Good Man in Africa* by one of my favourite writers, William Boyd. The place in question is the capital city of a West African country called Kinjanja. The country of Kinjanja and its capital, Nkongsamba, are both fictional, but they are skilful amalgams of many similar places.

Having found my extract, I then concocted a 'guide book' description of the same fictional place, in a kind of working-backwards exercise, using only the information found in the Boyd extract. The sharp contrast in styles is obvious, but what is so fascinating about the Boyd extract, is how he actually uses that basic material. Further comments follow the extracts.

The third piece is again my own concoction, using the same details about Nkongsamba, but this time written up as part of a romantic novel that is a million miles away in tone from William Boyd's black comedy. The rest of it hasn't been written yet, and may never be, but we'll call it *Forest of Love*.

## Extract 1 What the guide book tells us

Like most other ex-British West African countries, Kinjanja gained its independence in the 1960s and has been struggling to improve the standard of living for its rapidly increasing population ever since. The capital of Kinjanja is Nkongsamba, which lies in the coastal rain-forest belt to the south of the country. The site was chosen in colonial times because a series of low, sandy hills provided better drainage and some slight relief from the heat and humidity, which are high throughout the year. The town centre is easily recognisable by the mast of the TV studios, some office blocks and department stores. Outside this traffic-congested area the side streets are untarred and there is a zone of second-class housing with local markets, which soon merges with an even larger fringe of shanty towns.

The tone is neutral, impersonal. The facts are there, and no value judgements are made or invited. Now over to fiction.

In Chapter 1 of *A Good Man in Africa* we meet our anti-hero, Morgan Leafy. Described on the dust jacket as an escapee from suburbia, overweight, oversexed and not overburdened by worldly success, Morgan is supposed to be hard at work representing Her Britannic Majesty in Nkongsamba. Instead, we catch him casting a jaundiced eye over the town from his air conditioned office in the British High Commission:

**Extract 2 From *A Good Man in Africa***

Like Rome, Nkongsamba was built on seven hills, but there all similarity ended. Set in undulating tropical rain forest, from the air it resembled nothing so much as a giant pool of crapulus vomit on somebody's expansive, unmowed lawn. Every building was roofed with cor-rugated iron in various advanced stages of rusty ero-sion, and from the windows of the Commission – established nobly on a hill above the town – Morgan could see the rooftops stretch before him, an ochrous checkerboard, a bilious metallic sea, the paranoid vision of a mad town planner. Apart from the single rearing skyscraper at the town's centre, a bank, the modern studios of Kinjanjan Television and the large Kingsway general stores, few buildings reached more than three storeys. Most were randomly clustered and packed alongside narrow pot-holed streets lined with deep purulent drains. Morgan liked to imagine the town as some immense yeast culture left in a damp cupboard by an absent-minded lab technician, festering uncontrolled, running rampant in the ideal growing conditions.

Apart from the claustrophobic proximity of the buildings and the noisome cloying stench of rubbish and assorted decomposing matter, it was the heaving manifestation of life in all its forms that most struck Morgan about Nkongsamba. Entire generations of families sprawled outside the mud huts like auditioning extras for a 'Four Ages of Man' documentary, from wizened, flat-breasted grandmothers to pot-bellied pikkins frowning with concentration as they peed into the gutters. Hens, goats and dogs scavenged every rubbish pile and accessible drain bed in search of edible scraps, and the flow of pedestrians, treading a cautious path between the mad-honking traffic and the crumbling edges of the storm ditches, never ceased. . . .

. . . Of late, or at least for the last three months, it had cast him into a scathing misanthropy so profound that had he possessed a spare nuclear bomb or Polaris missile, he would gladly have retargeted it here. Blitzed the seven hills in one second. Cleared the ground. Let the jungle creep back in.

Boyd's choice of words and detail here is masterly. There is that bookish, slightly ironic 'undulating' near the beginning, and 'nobly', which is definitely ironic as used to describe the site of the Commission. But those apart, Boyd has selected every other adjective and verb with wicked glee for maximum negative impact. There is nothing 'nice', sympathetic or even neutral, about the entire piece. The result is a climax of weariness and disgust that is tragi-comic. We've met our man – surely this can't be the Good Man of the title? Now all we have to do is sit back and watch poor old Morgan sweat his way ungraciously through whatever this dreadful place is about to throw at him.

Yet can Nkongsamba be anything else but the posting from Hell that Morgan sees before him? Of course it can. Here comes Julia from *Forest of Love* and she's in a very different frame of mind. She's in love, or thinks she is. Could this possibly be the same town? The same continent?

## Extract 3 From *Forest of Love*

Not waiting to unpack, Julia went straight to the window, but was disappointed to find there was no way of opening it. Air conditioning, she thought. Who needs it? It separated you, insulated you, from the real life out there. Nkongsamba – the name even sounded like a dance. She'd written it on the airmail envelopes to Paul so many times – and now she was actually here.

On the way in from the airport, Paul had followed her fascinated gaze and seemed to dismiss the town with a shrug. 'Most of it's a dump – but the diplomatic area's OK.' Then he'd squeezed her knee and the damp warmth had instantly invaded her skin as if the limp cotton skirt had dissolved in the heat. 'At least we get a breeze up there if there's one going.'

Yet she was beginning to like the place. Hooting, honking, jostling, there was nothing planned or contrived about it, except perhaps for the TV mast and that gallant attempt at a skyscraper in the middle distance. It felt spontaneous – even friendly. It was a nothing-matching, come as you are, let's-do-it-in-the-road sort of place, with its crazy quilt of tin roofing in every shade of rust, and the forest beyond – a lush, primeval green.

There was life everywhere – dogs and goats, chickens and children, old grandmothers dozing in the sun. Even through the barred glass, a faint buzzing hum reached her, like some composite form of energy just waiting to be tapped.

'Coming, darling,' she said without turning at a rap on the door. Over dinner she'd ask Paul if they could go for a walk around first thing tomorrow.

So, from *Heart of Darkness* to Sweetness and Light – Nkongsamba can be all these things, but on any given day, it is what the writer wants it to be. The only way to achieve the desired effect is to be cunning with what you put in – and ruthless over what you take out.

It is also worth noting that this third extract has to do more work than the Boyd piece. *Forest of Love* would probably be a 45,000-word paperback for one of the romantic imprints or a magazine serial of roughly the same length. In this kind of fiction, no scene can be static. Julia may be in one place musing on her arrival, but the passage also tells us how she arrived, what she is doing there, something about Paul and what she wants to do tomorrow. It also implies that these two characters supposedly in love, have rather different ways of seeing things and introduces a creeping note of doubt about their relationship. On the other hand, *A Good Man in Africa* is a full-length novel of about twice that length. That kind of information can wait. The character of Morgan Leafy is absolutely central to everything that happens, as is the nature of Nkongsamba and his relationship to it. Therefore it is essential that the writer paints the picture fully for us without other distractions.

## Choosing your viewpoint

Getting the right viewpoint is crucial wherever your fiction is set. As viewpoint is a subject that raises a lot of heat and tends to worry experienced writers as much as beginners, it is perhaps worth reminding ourselves what it means.

Viewpoint is the position from which a story is told. It is in a sense the voice of the story, which is not the same as its style, although the choice of viewpoint heavily influences the style. The viewpoint tells us whose story it is.

The *first-person viewpoint* has an 'I' narrator, so that everything in the story has to be observed in a way appropriate to the 'I' character. This character can be the hero or heroine or simply an interested bystander or minor character in the main action. An interesting example of this type of viewpoint is *Rebecca* by Daphne du Maurier, where the 'I' is never actually named but engages our entire sympathy. Even Dickens didn't always get it right. In *David Copperfield*, David himself, the 'I' of the story, related events about his own birth in a way that is quite impossible in the circumstances.

A third-person viewpoint is less limiting, but may lack the intimacy of a first-person story. It can take several forms, from the personal third-person narrative style above where all the story, or large sections of it, are seen as a particular character such as Morgan or Julia would see them, to what is sometimes called the God viewpoint, where the whole story is seen from no particular character's perspective. Perhaps the ultimate extension of the third person viewpoint is when the author's all-seeing voice intrudes as asides of the 'so now we see, dear reader' variety.

Attempting an unusual viewpoint can add an extra dimension to a story, such as telling it from the perspective of, say, a pet or a building (often attempted by beginners and not always appreciated by some editors). Double and multiple viewpoints are now quite popular in novels, for example, *Hawksmoor* by Peter Ackroyd, and, again, *Brazzaville Beach*. Here, William Boyd gives us the further 'voice' in the form of a scientific commentary on topics relevant to the theme.

## That winning combination

For real impact, there is nothing quite like a story that could only happen in a specific place, at one particular time in its history, and then only to the people you have chosen to put there. Some of the most popular fiction ever written has this magic combination. One example would be *Gone With the Wind*. Certainly an historical novel, it is also a geographical one, being as deeply rooted in its location (the American South) as it is in its period (the Civil War). The unforgettable Scarlett, Rhett and Mammy are not merely products of their time, but of their homeland in all its aspects, from the red cotton soil of Tara to the bustling street life of Atlanta.

Another classic example of this winning combination is Graham Greene's *The Third Man*. Post-war Vienna was the perfect place for that strange collection of characters to come together – an English major, a beautiful refugee actress, the seedy Dr Winkle, and Holly Martin the American pulp novelist looking for his one-time friend, Harry Lime. Racketeering in penicillin drives the plot, and then Greene milks every aspect of the Vienna townscape for maximum dramatic and emotional impact – the crumbling, hollow grandeur of the apartments, the piles of rubble, the night-clubs, the fairground wheel, and of course the sewers.

The 'local colour' in some areas is so notorious that it seems to get in on every occasion. The Mafia in southern Italy and Sicily, drug trafficking in Miami and Colombia, diamond smuggling in South Africa or Tel Aviv, Triad gangs in Hong Kong, and until recently the espionage industry based round the Eastern Bloc countries are only the leaders in this field. Such linkage of places with their problems may be valid and almost unavoidable, but the dangers of over-exposure and clichéd situations are obvious. Go for an original treatment if possible and always bear in mind that if it's Amsterdam it doesn't always have to be tulips and windmills.

In your search for that winning combination, it may help if you specialise in one specific area – a place that has somehow got under your skin. You may already know where that place is, or you may still be looking, but you will know when it happens. In his song 'Rocky Mountain High', John Denver sings of 'coming home to a place you've never been before'. But nowhere is this sense of passionate involvement with a place that is *not where you are from* more movingly expressed than at the beginning of *Out of Africa*. After a luminous description of the air above the Ngong Hills near her beloved coffee farm, Danish-born Karen Blixen says:

> 'Up in this high air you breathed easily, drawing in a vital assurance and lightness of heart. In the highlands, you woke up in the morning and thought: Here I am, where I ought to be.'

Find a place which means as much to you as that, and you are halfway to writing a bestseller.

## 10

# BRINGING IT ALL BACK HOME

A Woody Allen character when asked if he thought sex was dirty gave the immortal reply, 'It is if you're doing it right'. When asked if writing is difficult, most writers would probably say the same. Tackling a full-length work is a daunting business and good short stories can be just as challenging in their own way, even when no special background research is required. The main difficulty with setting your work abroad is how to keep it all fresh in your mind once you are back home again. This chapter offers some help with that problem, with some final hints on making the most of what you know.

### Writing it up

Some people claim to have total recall, but the rest of us have to rely on a memory that is faulty, selective, and sometimes out to lunch. Most writers' main memory back-up system, latest technology not withstanding, is in the form of notes, particularly where travelling is involved. And notes, however neat and legible, have to be sorted out and filed for easy access as soon as possible on return.

Don't skimp on this. My own memory is so capricious that I sometimes come across a loose bit of scribbled information that has been forgotten so completely that I would deny any knowledge of it if it wasn't in my own writing. Sometimes the only way that I can remember anything about it is when it is near something else of similar vintage.

How you make notes is a highly personal matter, but if you feel unhappy about your own system, maybe some fresh thinking is in order.

Notebooks come in two kinds:

1. Those in some kind of binding which is meant to stay that way, like exercise books, the fancy sort with marbled covers and those you get given at Christmas called The Writer's Journal, Thoughts for the Day, diaries or similar.
2. The kind that are meant to have pages torn out – ring or wire bindings, tear-off pads and so on.

Some writers will use nothing but bound notebooks. They have one for each trip or major topic, in different colours and clearly labelled. Everything goes into the relevant notebook and usually stays there, to be looked up when required. Alphabetical indents are particularly useful here if you stick to the same system throughout – A for Art or Animals, F for Food or Flora, T for Transport or Themes etc, according to interest. Irrelevant letters can be amalgamated with overloaded ones. The whole book is then labelled *Turkey, 1993* or *Human Interest*, or whatever.

The advantage of a system like this is that re-writing and filing are kept to a minimum. The only thing I personally have against it is that the notebooks are often too big to be toted everywhere, and get very tatty if you try. They can also get lost, especially while travelling, which can be disastrous with an all-the-eggs-in-one-basket system.

The three-notebook approach suggested in Chapter 4 reduces this risk. To recap, this involves using tear-out-type notebooks of three sizes. One is the really tiny wire-bound type that fits into the palm. It will tuck into a shirt pocket, bum bag or beachwear with a diary pencil tied on for jottings on the hoof. A reporter's notebook will do at other times when space or weight is not so limited. Again keep a ballpoint tied to the wire rings to avoid rummaging in bags, and secure the pages with a rubber band to flip open easily. An A4 tear-off pad, lined or unlined and hole-punched, is kept back at base for longer material.

Back home, the notes can then be rewritten if absolutely necessary, but the easiest thing is to separate out most of the pages of whatever size and slip them into the relevant files. It may be a little extra work, but I find the loose-sheet system much more flexible in the end. It lends itself to cutting and pasting, cross-referencing and most other ways of keeping the things you want together, temporarily or permanently. For me it has the added advantage that when I eventually get around to sorting it out, it brings back the trip and reminds me of other things I should have put down.

This is not to say that using a cassette recorder as a notebook simply by speaking your mind into it or recording your guide's lecture isn't a very useful addition. But there are times when recording just isn't possible or appropriate, and most people will want to transcribe afterwards in case of accidental erasure. Writing tutors sometimes claim that relying on recordings instead of taking notes makes writers lazy, in that simply speaking is easier than finding the right words for writing. It is also said that recording your impressions can lead to a one-dimensional way of remembering things – but the same could perhaps also be said of photos, videos or good old-fashioned note-taking. A wise mix is probably best.

## Finding it again

Filing is the first task of every office junior – which is odd, because it is probably the most important job of the lot, including the managing director's. If something cannot be found it is worse than useless. If you have been a writer for more than a week, you will already know this. Like writing itself, filing is a highly individual thing where the best and worse of the personality soon shows. The problem is particularly acute for writers who travel, as they tend to accumulate so many extra bits and pieces – maps, photos, brochures, leaflets, postcards, pull-outs and clippings, pods and pebbles and heaven knows what else.

The main thing to remember is that filing doesn't have to be tidy – it just has to work. I have yet to find one single system that covers everything. I've got the lot: drop files in a four-drawer cabinet, box files, ring binders by the dozen, cardboard wallets, wooden fruit trays, plastic kitchen tidy baskets, old suitcases, carrier bags, and shoe boxes under the bed. I need variety, not just for all the odd shapes and sizes but to help me picture where things are. A friend swears by the archeological approach. Most used and recent material on top, the rest in layers beneath – which is fine as long as nobody sneezes, or worse, tries to tidy up.

What helps most is being able to keep wads of similar material separate from the rest within one file, box, wallet, or whatever. For this I have one simple ploy which is both cheap and environmentally friendly, if not very elegant. I keep all used, reasonably strong and undamaged A4 envelopes. Each is then trimmed on three sides, leaving one long side untouched. Folding it inside out produces an A4 blank folder which can be labelled with a felt pen and tucked inside any kind of holder except a ring binder. It works well for chapters in a book, individual short stories, episodes of serials, various drafts, and notes on different topics. I would go so far as to say that A4 envelopes recycled in this way probably keep me sane and in work. Ring binders I keep almost entirely for correspondence, as I find that not enough of anything else lends itself to hole-punching.

## Keeping it fresh

The amount of time between experiencing a place and starting to write will vary enormously. Some writers will already be halfway through the first draft by the time they get home. Others may take years before they feel ready. It may have something to do with the stress of travel or the rush of things that need seeing to on returning home, but I find that the first week or so is a bit of a blank. Two to three weeks after is the time when images of a place are at their most vivid. By then too, the photos are ready and that's when I get down to sorting it all out.

When I am ready to start work, one thing I find very helpful if I haven't done it as part of the preparation is 'setting up a corner' – the kind you see in primary schools – which says plenty about the way my brain works. The desk, the pin board over it, and the nearest mantelpiece or window sill are cleared of other clutter and the space devoted to the chosen location. Up go the maps, brochure pictures, snaps and anything that can be displayed in the way of samples and souvenirs.

Some other tricks for recapturing the mood are:

- playing tapes of local music
- going to a shop or restaurant associated with the place
- watching videos recorded previously or on the spot
- reading or re-reading a novel or memoir connected with it
- wearing something bought locally.

All this may sound foolish, but as mentioned in Chapter 2, it can work in all kinds of unexpected ways. One further example: I was stuck for the right atmospheric note on which to end a serial set in Thailand. Sitting cogitating at my machine, I was actually wearing a hilltribe silver necklace, a knick-knack I'd almost missed the Land Rover to get. On the pin board was a good quality brochure picture of a woman of the Akha tribe that featured in the serial. By now I knew that the Akha loved silver. In fact most of their costumes were decorated with silver balls and discs. The woman's necklace had three crescent-shaped plaques one below the other, and hanging from the last was a silver disc. My necklace had only three different-sized silver crescents but until then I hadn't realised their significance. The books hadn't mentioned it, but what I was seeing was the remnants of an ancient moon cult long predating Buddhism. So at the end of the story, the heroine is able to link seeing the new moon with

127

the Akha village women who played such a part in her life, and finds hope for their future and her own.

## Fictionalising real places

After all the effort of getting the details of any location correct, it may seem odd to suggest another possibility – that of fictionalising real places. We are not talking here about the immediate setting of the story, such as a house or business, a street, neighbourhood or small village because most writers do this anyway. It is more the larger places – a main town, district or whole country that concerns us. There are various ways of fictionalising real places, and it is not the same as inventing an imaginary place, for which see later.

One way is to base your fictional place almost entirely on one real one. The place names and a few details are altered, but the end result is still essentially recognisable. More usual is to use an amalgam of places that have a basic similarity, so that the readers know roughly where they are and what to expect. Examples include William Boyd's Kinjanja in *A Good Man in Africa*, or Malcolm Bradbury's Slaka in *Rates of Exchange* with its elements of several Eastern European countries.

There is a time-honoured tradition of fictionalising in this way, from Shakespeare's Illyria through all the Ruritanias, Barsetshires, Fitzrovias, Azanias and Ambrosias admired through the centuries. The advantages are numerous:

- More freedom to move the main features of the landscape or townscape to where they are most convenient for the story.
- A degree of protection for the author, against being sued perhaps, or being barred from entry next time if the authorities concerned take exception to a real place or its people being lampooned or criticised.
- More possibilities for humour or satire.

- A chance for writers to show off, perhaps to invent local languages or customs.
- Less checking is required and you can't really be accused of getting it wrong. Consistency within the model you have set up is all that is necessary.
- Easily pronounced and instantly recognisable place names with the correct local flavour can be used instead of jaw-breaking real ones.

Something may also be lost of course. Unless the writing is skilful, the reader may be too conscious that this is not a 'real place'. A feeling of fakery, of trying too hard, or even of farce can creep in unless place names and other details are chosen very carefully. Some authors duck out by not mentioning the main location by name at all – just 'the country', or 'the town'.

The trend today seems to be more towards using real places, warts and all. If some of the characters hold recognisable positions in these place – mayor, minister for whatever, chief of police, bishop and so on – it can be made clear that the time is 'the near future' in addition to the usual disclaimer at the front. There is less disbelief for the reader to suspend and the impact is more immediate. Michael Dobbs's *To Play the King* is a recent example.

## Inventing imaginary places

This tends to be the province of the fantasy and science-fiction writer. It is also particularly common in children's books. Some wonderfully imaginative examples include Lilliput, Wonderland, Oz, Narnia, and Never-Never Land. Some writers such as Tolkien have invented entire worlds with their own time systems and languages.

Many of these imaginary worlds are thinly disguised versions of our own. They reflect sometimes the best, sometimes the worst of what we like to think of as reality. One example is Terry Pratchett's Discworld. This delightfully absurd creation is carried by four giant elephants borne on the back of the star turtle, Great A'Tuin, as it swims through space. 'Magic glues the Discworld together – magic generated by the turning of the world itself, magic wound like silk out of the underlying structure of existence to suture the wounds of reality.' (From *Wyrd Sisters* in the Discworld series.) Magic indeed, and if you can conjure enough of it through the power of the written word, anything goes.

This kind of thing cannot be taught. Maybe some of it rubs off, in which case one piece of advice to would-be inventors is to become conversant with what else is around. Some writers in the field claim that they never do this, fearing 'contamination' of their own imaginary worlds. If you are confident enough of your own originality, that's all that needs to be said. But for the more cautious, it would be wise to check for overlapping and duplication. There is always the risk of being accused of plagiarism if you circle too near an established writer's imaginary patch.

If an explanation of the need to create imaginary or alternative worlds is required, Pratchett's phrase about suturing the wounds of reality can hardly be bettered. Often these imaginary worlds are born from some deep emotional scar or need of the author's that can only be guessed at – Wonderland and Never-Never Land being obvious candidates for the amateur psychologist's attentions. Their success lies in touching a similar need in others. J. M. Barrie said that it was not until years after writing *Peter Pan* that he realised what it was about.

Having said that, there is ample evidence that many writers draw on their own travels or reading for the scenic aspects of their creations. Barrie loved the works of Robert Louis Stevenson – hence the Redskins, the tropical treasure island and those wonderful pirates. In *Pyramids*, Pratchett has fun with the kingdom of Djelibeybi (best said aloud) which is based on ancient Egypt. While reading entries for a travel writing competition, I was struck by how many aspiring writers had an almost Road-to-Damascus experience at their first sight of, perhaps, Greece, the Nevada desert, the Russian steppes or the Australian outback. It was as if they were seeing the world and their place in it with new eyes. There was a strong sense that they could hardly wait to use the colours, the light, the sense of space, of ages past and of their own awe, in some new departure in their writing – perhaps for a novel, a space odyssey or fantasy.

## Avoiding bear traps

Inventing imaginary places is even safer than fictionalising real ones when it comes to the problem of accuracy. People can fly, the moon can be made of green cheese and trees can go for an evening stroll if you want them to. Back in the real world, however, getting it right is everything. It doesn't matter how remote the place, if you use it by name in your story, there will be someone out there dying to write in if you get one street name wrong. At least, it is wise to assume this is the case. You may get away with it once, but twice and your editor or publisher will not trust you in the same way again.

Unfortunately, there are many more ways of getting something wrong than there are of getting it right. Here are just some of them, with some possible remedies:

### Spelling of place names

Some places are positive nightmares in this respect, with Eastern Europe, Madagascar, Turkey and China high on the list.

- If several options are on offer, opt for an anglicised version if there is one.
- Go for the simplest spelling and/or the one the readers are most likely to recognise or read easily.
- Once you have decided, be consistent.

- Don't be too pedantic, and let the publisher have the last word.

## Wrong facts

There is no way round this except to check, check, check. This especially applies to the facts that are 'obvious' or the ones you think you know – see the cautionary tale below. Sometimes it is better to do without some snippet you thought was essential or work round it if checking is impossible, but too much of this and the work could lose its edge of authenticity.

## Misplacement

This is the geographical equivalent of an anachronism, that scourge of historical novelists. Instead of something being in the wrong time, it is in the wrong place. One famous romantic novelist was once taken to task for having a Tudor character refer to minutes and seconds. For the average Elizabethan, no concept of such small amounts of time existed. A classical anachronism, perhaps. A classical misplacement would be putting a tiger in Africa, where there are none in the wild.

Much has already been said about making sure things are in the right place, particularly in the chapters concerned with landscape, weather, plants and animals. It is particularly important to check if an exotic location is combined with an historical background.

There follow some cautionary tales combining elements of the above. For the beginning of a serial set in an Umbrian hill-town, I wanted the heroine to notice a man following her as she arrives at the airport. I assumed that Florence had an international airport and had her land there from England. (I'd arrived by train from Verona, myself.) It doesn't; the nearest international airport is Pisa – as a friend pointed out on reading the ms when it was already past the proof stage. I must admit I panicked. Yet I was so sure that I'd seen a direct flight to Florence on the board at some British airport. Frantic checking revealed that technically I was right. There are now some flights direct to Florence's domestic airport, Peretola, from Stanstead, where I'd recently been delayed myself and had plenty of time to study the departure board. Phew! But next time, I'll check *before* it goes to press . . .

Sometimes the spirit rather than the letter of the law is acceptable. I got the title for a serial set in Turkey from having my memory jogged by one of the Poems on the Underground so thoughtfully placed by London Transport to cheer weary commuters. It was an extract from The Song of Solomon – 'Rise up, my love, my fair one, and come away./For lo, the winter is past and the rain is over and gone, . . . the time of the singing birds is come, and the voice of the turtle is heard in the land.' 'The Voice of the Turtle' was a perfect title for a romantic story involving conservation of turtle nesting sites. I even worked the verse in as part of the storyline and was feeling pleased with the result. Then another voice intruded – the still, small one that says, Hang on, don't I remember something about a mistranslation? Sure enough the New English Bible revealed that it really should have been turtle *doves*. I chewed the carpet for a while, then eventually decided that if turtles were good enough for the King James version they were good enough for me.

## A fresh look at your own back yard

There is always a danger that at some point during this book, aspiring writers may begin to feel discouraged if exotic destinations are beyond their reach. So it is worth repeating the points made in Chapter 2, under Where have you been all your life?:

- The location doesn't have to be 'exotic' in the waving-palm-tree sense to work.

- Your experiences of it doesn't have to be recent. For older people, past memories are often the most vivid, and childhood memories are very persistent.
- With careful research and observation, a good writer can get as much from the frequently maligned package tour as from some unresearched back-packing foray to the edge of nowhere.
- Much of what has been said could be of help for using your own home ground as the location for your stories.

This last point deserves a little more attention. Many writers have been very successful in setting their work almost exclusively on their home patch. When the background plays a strong part in the stories, it can sometimes take on a character of its own, to the extent that a place may become associated with a particular author or book, and vice versa. Hardy's Wessex, the North East of Catherine Cookson, Daphne du Maurier's Cornwall and so on.

This degree of identification doesn't come easily. It is not enough for a writer simply to have lived in a place to use it effectively in fiction. Such success means that a great deal of research has been done. This is not just a matter of reading up. It includes an intimate knowledge acquired by talking to local people, watching the change of seasons, getting to know the area on foot, using maps and even making your own, and probably living there for many years.

To get the best out of your home ground, why not apply the techniques suggested for researching a foreign location? This is often best tackled after you have been away for a while. Try to see the place as if you were a tourist or a visitor from Mars. You could be surprised at what new perspectives you discover.

But it is not just a matter of research, even in its widest sense. It never is. What such 'regional' authors have is a passionate attachment to their home area. There may be a bit of love/hate in the relationship, but the deep emotional response is there. And it is precisely that which makes any place, near or far, come alive. Feel it, and you are ready to start.

# A SOCIALITE'S ABDUCTION

## WESTERN DESTINIES

### BLYTHE CARVER

# 1

—————

Matilda Holbrook, known as Mattie to her friends and family, looked around the large room at the guests. The Holbrook house was large, home to Mattie, her younger brother, Franklin, and younger sister, Lauren, as well as their parents, Judge Carter Holbrook and the respectable Mrs. Abigail Holbrook, who was a master at putting together parties just like this one.

Mattie's father had just presided over a big court case, one that decided the fate of two men accused of murder. The outcome had been what everyone considered justice, so a celebration was naturally called for.

The room was alive with guests, buzzing with

conversation, the clinking of glasses, the fragrance of pomp, circumstance, and money in the air, but all Mattie wanted to do was find Franklin. It wasn't that she wanted to spend more time with her brother—whom she truly did love—it was because she knew he would be with Michael. Michael Knowles, the best-looking boy in all of Bighorn, Texas, their home. It was also home to 7,000 other people, and probably at least a third of them were young men around twenty-one, which was her age.

That didn't matter to her. She was sure Michael would win all the prizes, should there ever be a contest for handsome men. He was a newcomer to Bighorn, and Mattie didn't know him well. Her first attempt at conversation with him hadn't gone well. She'd stuttered and said something silly about their names starting with the same letter. He'd just given her a blank stare before turning to Franklin with his eyebrows raised in such a way that made Mattie feel a bit humiliated.

She was determined to try again, and so, she was on the hunt for Franklin, who was friends with Michael.

She spotted the two young men on the veranda, holding drinks in one hand, the other in their pockets. Michael was talking. They weren't looking at each other. That is, Franklin wasn't looking at Michael, who was very animated in his speech, slinging the hand with the drink in it to the point that it was dangerously close to spilling its contents out all over the place.

Mattie couldn't decipher the look on her brother's face, as she could only see his profile. But what she did see was a set jaw and narrow eyes. To her, that meant Michael was saying something her brother objected to but was staying quiet out of politeness.

"Hello, you two," she said, stepping out of the house and strolling over to where the two men were standing. Michael's eyes were emotionless when he settled them on her. She felt a twinge of anxiety in her chest and looked at her brother instead. She instantly saw that he was unhappy. "I, uh, hate to do this, but I need your help, Franklin. Mother has asked me to bring up some more wine from the cellar, and I can't do it by myself. Will you kindly help me?"

"I would be more than glad to help you, Sis," Franklin said immediately, giving her a grateful look she was sure could only be seen by her. He abruptly handed his glass to Michael, who took it, looking slightly bewildered. "Great conversation, Mike. Sorry but I gotta go."

Mattie gave Michael an uncomfortable smile, mouthing, "sorry," as she dragged Franklin away by his arm. She didn't have to put much effort into it. He came quite willingly.

"What was that all about?" she hissed. "I could tell you were not happy standing there with him."

"He was spouting nonsense," Franklin responded hotly. "He's an aspiring lawyer with aspirations in politics, and you know how I feel about all that."

Mattie nodded, her stomach turning just a bit. She didn't want her brother to go off on one of his rants about politics. His goal in life was to be a doctor, and that had nothing to do with politics. She'd told him many times to stick with medicine, and she would be glad to hear anything he wanted to say about it.

"We need to find Lauren anyway," Mattie said quickly. "The speeches will start soon, and Mother and Father expect us all to be there to support them. You know how Mother feels about speaking in public."

He nodded. "She likes to have us all there. Not that she can see us from on stage with those lights in her face. We could be dressed like clowns, and she wouldn't know."

"I know," Mattie replied, nodding. "Don't think about that right now. Just help me find her."

Franklin nodded. "I'll check upstairs. You check down here and outside."

"Sounds good."

For the next twenty minutes, Mattie went through each room where there might be guests. She lived in a mansion, and there were plenty of rooms open to guests when a party was going on. Their house had a library, a game room, a billiards room, even a room Mattie considered a ballroom because of its size, though she was the only one who called it that, and no one ever referred to their parties as balls.

Finally, after searching the first level and the surrounding grounds as best she could, she stood at the end of the veranda. The sky had grown dark, and everyone had gone inside for the speeches. She hadn't seen her brother but assumed he had gone to the grand room where everyone had gathered to listen to her father, her mother, and their speaking guests.

She ran her eyes over the grounds. There were

only a few stragglers left, young couples wanting to spend time alone together.

She walked to the edge of the veranda and put her hands up on the waist-high stone wall that surrounded it.

Her heart jumped into her throat when a large hand went around to cover her mouth entirely. A second hand wrapped around her throat, and she found herself unable to move.

Words were hissed into her ear, leaving her feeling numb.

"You won't find your sister. We have her. You will receive a letter tonight. We will leave it right here. You will follow the instructions, or you won't see your sister again. Count to sixty before turning around unless you want to meet your Maker right now."

Fear paralyzed Mattie. She did as she was told, and when she finally turned, there was no one in sight, not even the couples who wanted to spend a little time alone.

## 2

"It's a good proposal, Dylan," Luke Turner told his best friend while examining the cocktail glass in his hand that was almost empty, "but you know what they're gonna say." He took a drink, looking at his friend over the rim.

Dylan Sullivan grunted. He knew exactly what his friend was saying and agreed with him, though he didn't want to admit it.

"Well... I don't see why we should need to be married to get a loan. Don't they realize we have fewer people to spend our money on, and they have a better chance of getting paid back?"

"Ain't how it works, Dylan," Luke replied, kicking his feet up on the coffee table in between them.

The two men were seated in Dylan's modest

living room, complete with a few side tables, two chairs, a couch, and a coffee table. Dylan wasn't interested in luxury living. He just liked to be comfortable. His home was far from dirty, as he had a woman come in to clean every other day. He kept himself just as clean, his clothes were immaculate and he dressed like a rancher, though he wasn't one.

Dylan was a writer. His time for the past five years of his twenty-four had been spent developing ideas for local newspapers and magazines. Now he had an idea of his own, and he and Luke were bent on making it happen.

"The thought of publishing our own magazine is intimidating," Luke said, putting voice to the thoughts Dylan had been having. "It's gonna take everything we have. You know those men down at the bank aren't going to want to give money to a couple of bachelors. They won't know what we plan to do with it. We can say one thing and do another. If you're married, they trust that you're making solid choices and will keep your word."

Dylan shook his head. "I know the policy. I just don't understand it. It doesn't make sense to me. Being married doesn't make someone more trustworthy."

"And I know that, too," Luke admitted, nodding. "Nothing I can do to change the policy, though."

"Well, I'm not looking for a woman in Bighorn. I've met every woman here, and I'm not interested."

Luke laughed. "You've met every woman in Bighorn? Really?"

Dylan narrowed his eyes at his friend. He knew full well Dylan hadn't met every single woman in their city. "I was exaggerating. But I don't have the time or inclination to go out searching for the ones I haven't met. They would just throw water on me anyway. I'm not a prowler."

"I've seen you do some pretty crazy things while exploring a new article."

"Not the same. I'm not dedicating my life to a woman I'm not in love with."

"What do you want to do then? They've already turned us down once. We've got nothing to show for them."

Dylan thought about it for a moment, plunging his hand through his shoulder-length wavy brown hair. He tapped his fingers on the coffee table in front of him. What was the solution, he wondered? Would a fresh start somewhere else make a difference? He couldn't leave his house behind, though. And he didn't want to move away from Bighorn.

He sighed loudly.

"I know," Luke said suddenly, snapping his fingers. "How about we take a vacation?"

Dylan snorted, his eyes on his friend. "We can't afford a vacation. We're trying to make money, not spend it."

Luke shook his head, leaning forward, his blue eyes sparkling with excitement. "No, no. I mean, we could go to Lincoln and see my uncle and aunt. They often support my endeavors. I get along with them well, and I know they would welcome us. We could talk to them about a loan or approach the bank there. I bet they would help us out."

Dylan felt an edge of happiness in his chest, and a smile came to his face. "Well, that sounds like a great idea. I'm anxious to start writing again. I didn't expect what happened the last time and I think it would be best if I kept what I'm saying to a specific magazine. I don't need women reading what I say and then throwing their little fits about it just because they don't like what they read."

He knew the look Luke was giving him. He'd seen it a lot. But he was determined. If men gave women enough control, things would go terribly awry. Women were emotional, irrational creatures that couldn't be trusted to make decisions for anyone but themselves and their children. Best to leave the handling of the nation, politics, and medicine to the men. That way, it would be done right.

Those were the feelings and expressions he'd put into his extensive article in the Bighorn Gazette.

It had been met with quite a lot of criticism, stirring up controversy. People—that is, women, with an occasional male sympathizer—wrote to the newspapers that published his article, expressing their disapproval in his stance and disappointment in the newspaper for publishing it.

He hadn't expected the backlash and decided then and there he would only publish his articles in a magazine of his own making—a gentleman's magazine dedicated to all things men, denouncing the push for equalization of women's rights. Women were the weaker sex, he espoused as often as he was able, and unable to make logical, sound decisions that could have an impact on everyone in the nation. Voting was out of the question, as far as Dylan was concerned.

Luke had been trying to ease his viewpoint on the matter for years. Two years, to be exact. That was when they had become partners. Before that, they'd grown up together, both sons of miners with loving mothers, both only children.

They'd become partners in an advertising company, purchasing their own printing press and a building from which to run their business. In two years, they had developed and printed thousands of flyers advertising local businesses.

The article Dylan had written that got a lot of talk had done a bit of damage to their business. A third of their clients sought services elsewhere. Luke was disappointed, but Dylan stuck his ground. It would take a miracle for him to change his views on a woman's place in society and in the home. He didn't expect that to ever happen.

"Write to your uncle and aunt," Dylan said, nodding. "Let's do that. I need a break from here anyway."

"I'll get Lucy to run the press while we're gone. What do you think, a month?" Luke sat forward and pushed himself to his feet. Their secretary, Lucy Balling, had all the knowledge she needed to run their company while they were gone.

"Yeah, let's do that."

Dylan also got to his feet. Their secretary had joined Luke in trying to change Dylan's views on women. He liked her. But she hadn't succeeded in that venture so far. Neither had Luke.

## 3

Mattie could see the veranda from her bedroom window. She was seated in the window seat, holding onto the sill, her eyes intent on the area where she was told the instructions would be left.

After the frightening encounter, she hadn't even gone to listen to the speeches. She hadn't searched for her brother either. She went straight to her room and tried to calm down. Who could help her? Who could she turn to?

For several hours, until all the guests were gone and her mother had come to ask if she was all right, she just sat there, her arms folded on her chest, thinking about her sister, wondering where she was and if she was okay. Was she harmed? Had they hurt her? The thought was devastating.

Fits of crying came and went. She had taken to the window seat early on. The veranda was lit by two lamps that stayed lit all through the night. They had three guard dogs, but they were kept at the front of the house. There was a great tall stone wall around the entire property, but it had been fitted with plenty of doors so staff and servants could come and go.

When Mattie's mother had come in to say good-night, Mattie had asked her about Lauren and been told—to her utter devastation—that Lauren had gone to stay with a friend overnight. Pressed on what friend, her mother just said she was very tired after the long day, and they would talk in the morning if Mattie had an objection to her sister's actions.

Fearing what might occur if she said what she'd been told, she kept quiet. Better to wait for the letter and have something to show for what she claims, rather than get anyone upset and panicked. Maybe she could take care of it on her own? It was worth a try.

Abigail Holbrook was a good mother. No one could deny that. She loved her three children more than anything. The same could be said about Judge

Carter. He was a loving father, provided not just monetarily for his children, but also emotionally.

The lamps illuminating the veranda flickered as if a breeze had blown through. Mattie narrowed her eyes, staring into the semi-darkness.

Chills erupted over her skin when she saw the shadow of a figure moving toward the spot she'd been standing. For a moment, she contemplated finding one of her father's guns and going out there to confront the person who had taken Lauren. But that would have been foolish. The accomplices would simply kill Lauren and be done with it.

The thought brought immediate tears to Mattie's eyes. She saw the figure put one hand into the pot of a tall plant outside the doors to the veranda.

Mattie jumped to her feet and raced across the room. She had already donned her robe and slippers so she would be ready when the time came to get the letter.

She dropped down the stairs two at a time, wishing she was small enough and brave enough to slide down the banister. But that was too much fun for this panicked situation.

Mattie hurried through the dark house, holding her own lantern high in the air so she could see where she was going. The grand room was sparkling clean, having been immediately seen to when the party ended and the last guest had left.

Mattie's eyes were focused on the potted plant outside the doors. The knobs felt cold in her hands when she pressed them and pushed both doors open. A cool breeze blew against her face, but it was only because of the motion of the doors. It was a quiet, still night with a bright moon, sparkling stars, and an otherwise clear sky. There wasn't a cloud to be seen.

Mattie plunged her hand into the dirt of the potted plant and brought out the letter with a trembling hand.

She stared down at it, her eyes tearing up. She couldn't believe this was happening.

She looked around to see if anyone might be watching, but beyond a few feet, it was too dark to see anything but shadows. Anyone could be out there, and she wouldn't know it.

With a pounding heart and ice-cold blood racing through her veins, Mattie grabbed the handle of one of the glass doors and yanked it open so she could get back inside. Suddenly, she didn't feel at all safe. She imagined a bullet whizzing through the air and striking her in the back.

She stood still on the other side of the glass door,

putting both hands up to her face and trying to breathe steadily.

"Get yourself under control, Mattie," she told herself aloud in a frantic whisper. "You have to be brave. You have to be."

She pulled in a deep breath and held it for a moment, her eyes closed. When she thought she could handle it, she set the lantern on a table near her and unfolded the note.

"Mattie."

Her name being called in the dark, silent room made Mattie scream and jump nearly out of her skin. She turned around, anger spilling through her, and hissed, "Franklin Holbrook, how dare you sneak up on me like that."

Franklin pulled his eyebrows together, examining her closely, his own lantern, bringing out the curiosity on his face.

"I've been sitting here watching you, Mattie. I was wondering what you're doing. What is that in your hands? Who are you talking to?" A teasing smile came to his face. "Are you seeing someone on the sly, sister dear? Will there be wedding bells soon, perchance?"

Mattie scowled. "No, there won't be wedding bells soon, Franklin," she replied in a heated voice.

"You should have told me you were there. It's not nice to scare the living daylights out of someone, you know. You should be smacked for that."

Mattie and Franklin typically got along. But Mattie's concern for her sister was making it hard for her to control her emotions. She debated for only a few moments whether she should involve Franklin before deciding she better. He wasn't the law. Surely the kidnappers wouldn't care if she recruited him to help her with the task the bandits were placing on her?

She flapped the letter in the air toward him. "This is what I'm here for, Franklin. Someone has taken Lauren."

It was Franklin's turn to frown. "What are you talking about? She's at Rose's, staying the night. Mother told me so."

Mattie shook her head violently, gesturing with one hand for him to come over to her. "No, she's not. Look. Someone grabbed me earlier and told me they would be leaving instructions. That they took her and if I don't follow these instructions, they will kill her. Mother and Father will be destroyed if something happens to Lauren. You have to help me. We can't let them know about this."

Franklin looked doubtful. He came over to stand

next to her, and they both bent over the lantern to read the letter she held up.

*Take the 814 train.*

*You are to stop the train near Trumperton.*

*We will board and collect the bounty from the passengers.*

*If you fail to stop the train or tell anyone about this plan,*

*you will never see Lauren alive again.*

Tears stung the back of Mattie's eyes, threatening to spill over and prevent her from seeing anything clearly. She turned away from her brother, dropping the letter to the desktop. He picked it up.

"We have to do as they say," he said quietly. "I will come with you."

"But how are we supposed to stop the train?" Mattie asked in a frantic voice. "I've never even seen anyone stop a train before."

Franklin gave her a sober look. "We'll figure it out, Mattie. We'll get her back."

**4**

---

Dylan clucked his tongue as he and Luke walked past a newspaper stand. He stopped briefly, taking one from the stack on the edge of the tabletop and flipping a coin to the boy behind the booth, who caught it smoothly.

"Thanks, Mister," the boy said with enthusiasm.

Dylan nodded at him as he stepped away, rejoining Luke on the walk to the train station. Luke got along well with his relatives—truth be told, Luke got along well with everyone, being naturally friendly and gracious—and they had agreed to let him and Dylan stay with them for a month. Luke's uncle was wealthy and popular—just like his nephew on the latter, not like his nephew on the former.

"Look at this," he said, snapping the paper so it was flat in his hand and they could both read the cover story. He tapped the back of his fingers against the picture on the cover. "He gives an awful lot of credit to his wife in this article. Even the title suggests she has anything at all to do with his success. Judge Carter Sage Holbrook celebrated by his loving wife, Abigail, and children while friends look on. That's too much. What did she have to do with his becoming a judge and having all that money, I ask you? What?"

Luke gave his friend a sardonic look. "Give it a rest, Dylan. He's a good judge. I've seen him in action. He's fair and doesn't react harshly. He looks at all the facts before he makes decisions."

"I wasn't talking about him, Luke," Dylan replied, stepping up to the platform just outside the train station. "I was talking about his wife."

"She loves him," Luke replied simply. "You've never been loved. You don't know what it's all about."

Dylan felt a bit of resentment and frowned at his friend. "What do you mean? My parents showed me all the love in the world."

"Yeah, but I'm not talking about that kind of love, am I?" Luke retorted. This was a regular argument between the two friends. Luke had outright told Dylan on many occasions that he simply didn't believe Dylan felt the way he kept posturing he did. Women were beautiful, he said, many were intelligent, just as many as men, and Luke personally knew several couples where the woman was a far cry smarter than the man she was with.

In truth, Dylan was waiting to be proven wrong. In all his life, he had never seen an instance where a woman proved to be better than a man in any situation. Other than giving birth, there was nothing a woman could do better or smarter than men. Not in his experience.

He prided himself on being the kind of man who had an open mind. He explored different avenues of thought but had yet to come up on a woman who could match wits with him. To him, that meant it was too risky to give them the same equality as men as far as making decisions was concerned. They simply weren't built to make decisions. They were built to have children, cook, clean the house, and otherwise do tasks that men needed them to do.

They weren't much good otherwise, were they?

The one thing Luke had right was that Dylan

couldn't dispute was that he had never been in love, nor had a woman expressed any love for him. He knew his mother didn't count. He just said that to Luke to get under his skin.

He often wondered what it would be like to be loved by a woman, to be truly cared about, to see the look of longing and affection in the eyes of a woman. He didn't object to women in general. Just their insistence that they have a higher place in society than they did.

"I'm gonna go in and get the tickets," Luke said under his breath as if he was only reminding himself instead of notifying Dylan why he would suddenly be gone.

Dylan nodded, watching his friend walk toward the door of the station, a small building only suitable for a town half the size of Bighorn. He dropped his eyes to the article about the judge and read through it. The train whistled in the distance, and he looked up briefly.

There were plenty of people on the platform waiting to take the train to their preferred destinations. He scanned some of them, not recognizing anyone. A train station expansion was desperately needed. Perhaps that was something he needed to bring up to the city council. Maybe he should go into politics.

He snorted and dropped his eyes back to the paper, settling them on the photograph of the judge and his wife. He wasn't at all interested in that. He was a writer. That's what he planned to stick with for the rest of his life.

Luke came back with the tickets, but the two men stood back and let everyone else board before them. Neither were concerned about where they were seated and didn't need a private cabin. When everyone else had boarded, and the attendant was staring at them expectantly, they boarded.

Luke had to jostle Dylan's arm to get his attention because he'd resumed reading the paper, leaving the article about the judge and going on to the next interesting one.

"You gonna write for them?" Luke asked, looking down at the paper in his hands as they moved down the narrow corridor in between the sets of cabins where people were already seated.

"Nah," Dylan responded. "I've got a mind to do my own thing now. I don't want my articles approved by anyone above me. I want to write and publish whatever I want to write and publish. That's my right, isn't it?"

Luke nodded. "Course it is. How about this one?" He stopped in front of a closed door with the curtain on the inside of the window pulled up. There were two people sitting inside, but Dylan couldn't see them well because of the sunlight coming through the window on the other side of the cabin. They were sitting across from each other.

"Yeah. I don't care." He agreed, nodding.

Luke pulled the door to the side and poked his head in. "Mind if we sit here?"

Dylan was behind Luke as the two entered the cabin. There was no answer from either of the occupants, but he noticed when the young man's eyes widened and flipped to the woman sitting across from him. She had on a brown cape, and the hood was pulled forward so far, Dylan could only see the ripples of auburn hair coming out from under it.

He saw the brief and almost unnoticeable shake of her head, and the young man across from her averted his eyes out the window, never answering Luke's question.

Dylan shared a curious glance with Luke, and they both sat down, Dylan next to the man, Luke next to the woman. He was dying to talk to Luke about them and almost asked if Luke wanted to go with him to the dining car before the train got back underway. But his thoughts were interrupted by the loud train whistle and the attendants calling down the corridors and outside on the platform that the train was ready to go.

His eyes went out the window. He watched as the station moved out of view, and he saw the city from a distance as they pulled away.

"You're gonna love my Uncle Bernard, you know," Luke said.

"Can't wait to meet him," Dylan replied. "You talk such good things of him. I'm sure we will be friends right away."

## 5

**M**attie couldn't believe it when the two men entered their car. It obviously scared Franklin, who couldn't even give them an answer about coming in. What was he supposed to do? He stood no chance in a fight against either of them.

She hated that her first thought was one of danger. Under normal circumstances, she and Franklin would start a conversation with the men, find out everything about them they could during the time they had allotted to them between there and where they were going.

But these were far from normal circumstances. Her heart was pounding a mile a minute. Her blood felt like ice. She was repeatedly struck with anxious chills sliding over her skin. What would happen when she stopped the train? Her research with her brother had told her that there were emergency cords she could pull on in each car, and it would apply an emergency braking system, alerting the engineer so he could apply the full brakes.

The thought of what she was supposed to do frightened her more than anything in the world. Almost anything. Coming up on the body of her sister, that would be worse. That would be the worst thing that could ever happen.

Mattie wasn't used to being assertive. She wasn't a wilting lily but had never been put in a position where she needed to use her strength, her wits, her brain to such an extent as this. It wasn't until the night before that she'd realized how peaceful her life had always been.

The men were talking between them. She learned that they were friends, going to visit the relatives of one of them and that they were trying to get money for a new venture, a magazine they wanted to publish.

When one of the men—tall with broad shoulders and a muscular chest, his brown hair waving down to past his neck—said something about it being a magazine for men, she was curious what that meant.

She tried her best to quell her curiosity but found it impossible when he said, "I don't think many women would want to read it, even if they could."

Mattie's eyes narrowed and darted to the man's face. She didn't fail to see her brother eyes giving her a warning glance.

"I'm sorry, but what do you mean, even if they could?" she asked, trying not to bite the words at him.

He turned his head and gazed at her. Just that look made her heart thump harder, this time for a new reason. He looked amused, which enraged her even more.

"There are many women who don't know how to read or whose husbands won't let them read a magazine."

She couldn't believe how offended she was by his words. "Are you saying that kind of behavior is all right? And that it's somehow the woman's fault?"

"I'm saying that women have a place in society and shouldn't try to insert themselves into a man's world."

Mattie's jaw clenched. Her eyes averted to her

brother, who was subtly shaking his head. He didn't want to be involved, she could see that. But she wanted to say something to the man to put him in his place. She wanted to tell him where he could go with his ideas.

But she was a lady, the daughter of a judge. She would never embarrass her family in such a way. This man was obviously a writer. What would he write about her?

"I think you have a very archaic way of thinking," she replied, keeping her voice calm. "Women are just as capable of making their way in this world without a man as a man is without a woman. I see you aren't wearing a ring. Can I safely assume you aren't married?"

The man shook his head. "I'm not married."

"Do you ever plan to be?"

He looked disturbed, his eyes darting to his friend. His lips twitched, and she couldn't tell whether he was trying not to smile or frown. His eyes certainly reflected a frown. "I don't know what will happen in my future. I'm open to all possibilities."

"Well, I can guarantee you, sir, that you will not find a woman who will truly love you if you have that thought process. Your disdain for women will show through. You will never have anything but false love. Keep that in mind the next time a woman is nice to you, and you are rude in return."

The man's dark eyebrows shot up, slightly wrinkling his forehead. "I was not rude to you, madam. I don't even know who you are, though you do look familiar. May I ask your name?"

Mattie's cheeks flushed hot. She knew she had made a mistake. She shouldn't have opened up a conversation with the man. She dare not look at her brother. She knew the look that would be on his face. It would be that *look what you did* expression he always got when she said stepped over the line.

"You can ask," she said, thinking quickly.

He hesitated, glancing once again to his partner before settling his brown eyes on her once again. How could a man with views like his be so good-looking?

She didn't want thoughts like that going through her head. He had a despicable outlook on women. He was a chauvinist. She didn't like or appreciate men who tried to hold women back from reaching their full potential.

"Well, I'll kick things off, then. I'm Dylan Sullivan, and this is my business partner, Luke Turner.

We're on our way to Lincoln, which I'm sure you already heard, to visit his uncle and the family."

He held out his hand to her. She looked at it but didn't take it. She couldn't introduce herself to him. She was set to pull the emergency cord and stop a train. She should have just kept her mouth shut.

The awkward silence seemed to go on forever.

"Okay, I don't think she's going to tell us her name. How about you, sir? You're with her, I take it. I've seen the looks you've been sending her way. I'm of the mind you agree with what I've been saying. You obviously don't want her talking to us. Don't worry. We won't hurt her. Or you. We're friendly. Isn't that right, Luke?"

"Yep," Luke responded, nodding vigorously.

Mattie looked from one to the other, though she was keeping her head down. She couldn't possibly regret opening her mouth more. But when Franklin responded, she was suddenly proud of herself and him, whether they should have been keeping a low profile or not.

"I do not agree with what you've said, sir, and I'll thank you to leave that opinion to yourself. I am a man and won't be reading your magazine. I'm sure it will be filled with lies and insults against women. I appreciate and love women. I'll have nothing to do with it, thank you."

"Ah," Dylan said loudly, doing a slow clap for Franklin. "Bravo. Sticking up for the woman. I'd say," he moved his eyes between Mattie and Franklin, "brother and sister, aren't you? You look too much alike not to be."

"Please just stop talking to us," Mattie cried out, though she did it in a restrained way, so it came out not very loud.

"I beg your pardon, Miss," Dylan said, that amusement that she hated so much back in his voice. "I do believe you intruded on a conversation between myself and my partner here. I don't remember inviting you to speak to me. But since you've asked so nicely and said please, we will do as you ask."

"Let's go get a drink," Franklin said suddenly, jumping to his feet and holding his hand out to her.

Mattie took it gratefully, and they both left the compartment behind, Dylan's chuckling trailing behind her down the corridor, filling her chest with angry tension.

**6**

---

"Well, well, well," Dylan said, watching as the brightest spirit he'd seen in a long time sauntered out the door, her brother pulling her along by the hand, a very disapproving look on his face. Dylan wasn't stupid. He knew that look wasn't disapproving of the sister but of him and his beliefs.

"You love to antagonize people, don't you?" Luke asked, shaking his head. "Love to stir up trouble."

"I'm not stirring up trouble," Dylan replied defensively. "She was asking for it. She shouldn't have gotten in the conversation."

Luke shook his head again, this time closing his eyes for a moment. "You know what the problem with you is,?"

Dylan lifted one eyebrow and gazed at his friend. "I'm sure you're going to tell me."

"You don't respect anybody."

"Sure I do," Dylan was quick to respond. "I respect you. I respected my parents and my teachers."

"You respected the men who taught us. At the academy where there were no female teachers."

"I had respect for my female teachers, too."

Luke shook his head once more, clucking his tongue against the back of his teeth. "Yeah, when you were a kid. Look, Dylan, you're a great fellow. You're smart and good-looking according to the women I've talked to about it, which hasn't been many, so I'm really just assuming here, and you are really good at making money and finding ways to get money when you need it. I like being your friend. But it embarrasses me when you treat ladies like that. They aren't second class, you know. They are just as important to basic human happiness as a man is. In fact, no man would ever make me happy the way a woman would. They have a unique and valuable purpose."

"Of course they do." Dylan had to agree with his friend on that point. He had no doubt that they were valuable. "My problem isn't that they exist, and I don't think they are less valuable than men. I just don't think they should be getting involved in things that require logic and strength in here." He tapped his chest and moved his fingers to his temple. "They can't tell the difference between acting with the heart and acting with the brain. Everything they do comes from an emotional point of view. How can we trust the nation or even our own personal health to someone who can't think without involving their emotions? Sometimes it takes a heavy hand, a hand that women simply don't have."

Luke had turned his eyes to look out the window while Dylan was talking. He could see his friend wasn't in agreement with him and wondered when things had changed. While they were at the academy together, their fathers having been excellent friends who attended that same academy themselves, he and Luke had completely agreed that women should hold no place in government and should not be able to make decisions that affect the entire country, the state or even the town they live in.

At twenty-four, they'd been out of the academy for five years and during that time, neither had a love interest. Luke was followed and admired in many places they'd gone. But he'd never settled down with a woman. His reasons were his own, and he'd never indulged Dylan with them. Not that it made a difference to Dylan.

Until now. Now his best friend didn't agree with him.

"I can see you don't agree. What are you thinking?" Dylan had to press Luke. He was always interested in listening to someone else's point of view.

Luke hesitated and then sighed, turning his eyes slowly back to his friend. He shifted in his seat, looking uncomfortable.

"I just don't understand how you don't see what you just did. You were rude to the woman, and she and her brother left the car because of it, claiming to need a drink. I reckon I would need a drink after being treated with such disrespect."

Dylan was stunned. He purposefully let his mouth drop open as he widened his eyes. "You must be joking with me, Luke. You were saying those very words not long ago."

Again, Luke looked like he was uneasy with the conversation. That was a first for Dylan. He and Luke were usually in agreement about everything. Nearly everything, anyway. But not this topic. It was something they'd always shared. Their belief was that women were perfectly capable of holding intelligent conversations—some of them anyway—and that they would not qualify and should not qualify for any place that is in charge of anything or anyone else other than their children. They would bring their emotions into it and ruin everything.

Their fathers had agreed on that and told their boys it was so.

What had changed?

"I was wrong," Luke stated bluntly. He now had his gaze directed on Dylan with great intensity. "I was wrong, and I've had time to rethink my position. I do believe they can be trusted to make decisions, just as much as any man. Surely you aren't suggesting there are no stupid men out there. That there are no men that do vote, and they do so under unintelligent, immoral, and unethical pretenses. You can't tell me that. Because I've met some of our opponents on the other side in government, and let me tell you, there are idiots on both sides."

Dylan stared at Luke, unable to believe he was hearing those words from his friend.

"Granted, but—"

"No buts about it, Dylan," Luke interrupted him. "This all comes back to showing respect. Basic human respect. Just because the woman feels the need to stand up for her gender doesn't mean you get the right to berate her for it."

Dylan could tell he had irritated Luke with his banter with the woman. Although it caught him by surprise, and he was stunned to hear Luke's objections, he couldn't help questioning whether or not he had, in fact, been rude to her. He hadn't even thought about it.

"If you feel that strongly about it," he said, "I'll apologize when they come back in."

"*If* they come back in," Luke retorted.

"Look, I'm sorry, okay?"

Luke sighed, a look of acceptance on his face. "Just apologize to her and in the future try not to be so mean-spirited with your opinions. It's not nice."

Dylan felt appropriately scolded. He didn't like feeling that way, especially when the person who had called out his bad behavior was his best friend, someone who knew him better than anyone and would give him more leeway than anyone else. He strongly felt that if Luke thought he was being rude —well, he was probably being rude.

Duly reprimanded, Dylan went quiet, reviewing the conversation with the young woman in his mind and trying to see it from another point of view. He did hope she would come back in. He wanted to say he was sorry for disturbing her and being presumptuous.

They didn't come back right away, and Dylan got lost in thought. He'd enjoyed sparring with her and probably would have antagonized her a little more just to see the spark that came from her eyes when she spat her words of defense at him. It gave him a thrill. He hadn't thought it was hurtful to her.

The more he thought about it, the more he realized that he'd been approaching it from the wrong direction. He wouldn't want anyone poking fun at him that way either and irritating him on purpose.

Luke was right, he concluded. He'd been a cad, and he would have to apologize to the woman and her brother—or cousin—or whoever the young man was.

## 7

"I don't know why you have to go talking to those men like that, Mattie," Franklin hissed as soon as they left the compartment behind. "I usually understand, but today? Of all days, Mattie. Of all days. This is no time to be involving someone else."

"I couldn't help it," Mattie insisted, though she did feel a great deal of regret. "I don't like it when men like that say women have no place in society other than the domestics. We are just as capable of holding higher positions as men are. I don't—"

"*I* don't want to *hear* this," Franklin cut her off. "Please, Mattie. You know I don't feel like that, so I don't need you preaching to me about that stuff. Okay? Please."

"I'm sorry," she said softly. "I didn't mean to cause a problem."

"It's all right," Franklin replied gently. "Come on. Let's go get a drink. Maybe that will calm your nerves."

"I shouldn't. I should be keeping my wits about me."

"You don't want to go doing anything like this without a little bottled encouragement, Sis," he responded, his hold on her hand relaxing the further they went down the corridor.

The dining car was three to the back, in the middle of the train. Mattie and Franklin took two seats around a very small table, and after only a moment, Franklin got back up and went to the counter to get drinks for them both.

Mattie turned her eyes to look out the window, taking in the scenery as it passed at a fast pace. She flicked her eyes, focusing on trees, buildings, animals as they passed. She didn't want to think about what she was supposed to do when they got near to Trumperton.

She and Franklin had dug out their father's train maps and rolled them all out until they found the train going from Bighorn to Lincoln. They were supposed to look for mile marker 7 as soon as they got into Tennessee state lines. Trumperton was the first town, and Lincoln was fifty miles past that. They'd calculated it with one of their father's tools. They'd barely managed to get out of his study before he came in.

Franklin came back with a small glass and set it down in front of her. "Just some sweet sherry. I'm sure you have no objection to that, do you?"

"No," Mattie said shortly. "I'd go for several shots of bourbon right now. I don't know if I can go through with this, Franklin." Mattie wasn't used to feeling helpless and controlled. It was a feeling she detested and had avoided all her life. As a judge, her father was known to be one of the most fair-minded in the country. She had no doubt he would rise in the ranks to be nominated to the Supreme Court someday if that's what he wanted.

He'd raised all his children to believe that all men were created equal, regardless of their skin color, gender, or wealth. He treated everyone with the same amount of respect, regardless of their station in life, from the president to the maid.

Those were the beliefs that Mattie held, as well, believing them to be inherent to all human beings, even though some seemed to be more concentrated on themselves than others.

"You *can* do this, Mattie," Franklin stated firmly, reaching over as he sat down to put one hand on her shoulder. He squeezed her and gave her a look of confidence. "I know you can do it. I'm here with you. We have to save Lauren. We have to do it before our parents notice she's gone. They won't check until tomorrow, and I doubt Rose even knows they think Lauren's with her."

"You didn't speak to them before we came here, did you?" Mattie asked.

Franklin narrowed his eyes and pinched his lips together. "Of course not, Mattie. We wouldn't be here right now if I had."

Mattie shook her head. "I meant Rose and her family. You didn't see them while you were out today, did you?"

"No. I only went to the train station and bought the tickets. I didn't see anyone of note."

"Really?"

Franklin nodded, taking a sip from his drink. She noticed he'd gotten what looked like bourbon to her and was sipping it very slowly. She enjoyed sherry, so she drank hers with fervor. It made her head feel a little lighter. Franklin was right anyway. She could feel the courage filling her as she drank it.

Franklin cleared his throat and sat forward, his

eyes on the table and his hands clutching the glass between them.

"Mattie, what are we going to do after you pull the cord? And how are we going to do anything with those two men in the cabin?"

"We could go on in another car."

Franklin shook his head. "I looked. Didn't see even one car without passengers."

Mattie's heart sank. This was a popular train to take, the first one of the day, and the bandits probably timed it that way on purpose. The robbery would have been useless if there weren't any people on the train to rob.

The dining car itself was quite full. They would be hauling in a lot.

"I'll figure something out. I have to."

"You will. I know you will." She was encouraged by the sound of confidence in his voice. He was still looking down at the table, but he reached over and placed one of his hands on hers. When she looked up at him, he looked up at her.

"We're going to get her back. I know it. We have to. But I want to ask you something, and I don't want you to get mad at me for it."

Mattie's anxiety shot through the roof. She felt herself tense up from head to toe. "What is it?" she asked, hoping he wasn't going to ask the question that had been haunting her all night and that morning.

"You don't think Lauren was somehow mixed up with these men, do you? Didn't she seem a little odd to you at the party last night?"

Mattie tried to remember what time she'd spent with her sister at the party. They had gotten ready together. But once the party was under way, they hadn't stayed together.

"While we were getting ready, she talked about a young man she hoped to see at the party," Mattie said quietly, remembering, "but there's no way for us to know if he was one of the bandits or not. I mean, I reckon he could have been. That would have made it easy for them to take her away."

"I don't want to think she'd put herself in that position," Franklin mumbled, turning his eyes to the passing scenery outside the window. "But I can't help it. I think she's more vulnerable to that than any girl I've ever known. She's so wild. So reckless."

"I agree," Mattie said, "but we have no choice right now. It doesn't even matter if she knew the bandit. Maybe if she does, he would treat her better than he might a regular kidnapped victim."

Franklin's eyebrows shot up. "A regular kidnap victim? That sounds really awful."

Mattie just nodded. "Yeah, it does."

"I'll tell you what. Let's just ride the train in here until we get to Tennessee. When we hear the announcement, we'll go back to the car."

Mattie nodded. "Yes, I like that plan. Let's do that."

## 8

Dylan looked up when the young woman and her brother came into the cabin over an hour later. They sat down where they had been. The woman was holding a cup of hot coffee and had pulled her hood so far forward he couldn't see her face anymore at all.

"Pardon me, Miss," he said quietly, not looking at Luke, though he wanted to. "My friend pointed out that I might have been... well, I was very rude to you before you left. I do apologize. I hope that you can forgive me for overstepping and being condescending."

She turned her head only for a moment, looking at him with troubled eyes. He wondered what was going on behind that distraught look. Surely that couldn't have been because of him. He didn't have that kind of power over anyone. Not with his words.

Did he?

He felt an uneasy tension in his chest. If he had to identify it, he would have said it was guilt. Hadn't he felt guilty before? Why did it seem like such a strange feeling to him? He'd never felt that way when he'd stated his beliefs before. Why was she any different?

When she looked away from him, he felt dismissed. He didn't like that feeling. It made him angry. He opened his mouth to protest what he conceived as her being rude to him when Luke spoke up.

"Dylan," Luke stated his name firmly, "when we get to Lincoln, the first thing we should do is hire a buggy. It will take us to my uncle's house, and he will give us horses. We'll get his buggy driver to take the buggy back. How's that sound?"

Dylan turned his gaze to his friend, pulling his eyebrows together. He wasn't allowed to be rude to her, but she could be rude to him? When he locked eyes with Luke, he could practically hear his friend's words in his mind.

*She doesn't have to forgive you*, he heard Luke stating. *She doesn't even have to talk to you.*

Dylan pulled in a deep breath through his nose and held it for a moment before letting it out the same way, slowly and quietly. Why did he even want this woman to talk to him? Why was he seeking her forgiveness at all? Why did he care?

He let out a quiet harumph before shuffling his feet and pulling a pamphlet from his front pocket to distract himself from the ride. He'd brought it to remind himself what he was trying to do and what he wanted to accomplish. The pamphlet was one of the first he and Luke had published. It always made him feel good to look at it. It was one they'd created to advertise their own advertising company. As far as he was concerned, it was their best creation yet.

Dylan sighed, tapping the pamphlet against his hand, looking up but not directly at anyone else. He let his eyes roam around the small cabin, looking at nothing in particular.

"It's going to be a long, quiet ride for another fifty-five miles to Lincoln."

The next few minutes felt like an eternity to Dylan. He actually had no idea how quickly or slowly the time was passing. All he knew was that something had gone terribly wrong.

"Fifty-five miles?" the young man said in alarm. "Mattie. It's fifty-five miles to Lincoln."

Dylan frowned, watching as the woman and the man suddenly came alive with action. The woman whipped the hood off her head and peered through the window.

"It can't be. We couldn't have."

"Pull it. Pull it."

The coffee cup went crashing to the ground, splashing hot liquid around the woman's feet. She didn't seem to notice.

"Oh, no. Oh, no," she cried out.

"Pull it! Pull it!"

The next moment, Dylan watched as the young man rose from his seat and threw himself across to the other side. He wrapped both his hands around the long, thick cord of the emergency brake.

"No," Dylan and Luke yelled at the same time.

They both leaped up to stop the young man from pulling the cord, but Mattie rose to her feet, blocking them.

Her brother used all his weight to drop the cord down to its fullest length.

Immediately, the sound of the brakes applying in complete emergency mode blasted through the air. Dylan slapped his hands over his ears and lowered his head as his body tumbled across to the other side of the cabin.

Luke caught him before he could smash into him and shoved him off. Both men tumbled to the ground. Dylan felt something sharp in his ribs and cried out. He looked down in the chaos and saw the girl had fallen on him and was struggling to get up.

He put both hands firmly on her shoulders and lifted her off him. He was astonished to see she had tears streaming from her eyes. She was mumbling quickly in panic. The four of them were all over each other, trying to right themselves.

A gunshot in the near distance rang out the moment the brakes brought the train to a halt. Dylan's heart raced frantically. His eyes darted to the door and then to Luke, who had obviously also heard the shot. The sound of screams coming from another car alerted them that something had gone terribly wrong.

"What's going on?" he yelled out, pushing Mattie off him. "What did you do?"

"Franklin." Mattie was calling out to her brother. "Franklin. Franklin!"

"I'm right here, Mattie. Come on. Come to me. I'm right here." He sounded as panicked as his sister.

Dylan caught sight of them lurching toward each other. Franklin grabbed Mattie's hand, and he pulled himself up to his feet first and then his sister after.

"We have to get out of here, Mattie," Dylan heard the young man hiss. "We have to get out of here now. They will find us. But we have to get out of here."

"What about Lauren?" the young woman cried tearfully. "We won't know—"

"Come on. No more. Don't say anymore. We have to get out of here."

Dylan had, by that time, pushed himself to his feet. He held out a hand to Luke, who grabbed it and was on his feet a second later.

"They've got the right idea," Luke said quickly, watching as the two younger people ran through the door into the small corridor outside, glancing to the left and running to the right. "Let's get out of here. I'm not losing my life or my money to some lowlife train-robbing bandits. Come on."

Sounding like the young man Mattie had called Franklin, Luke opened the door the rest of the way, as Mattie and her brother had only opened it half-way. He looked to the left and the right. Dylan came up behind him, sticking his head out as well.

The screams of the other passengers were coming from the left. There were a few more gunshots. Dylan hoped and prayed they were just warning shots. He didn't want to believe anyone was actually being shot because that would mean the girl and her brother were responsible for the deaths of those passengers. They had been the ones to stop the train. They had let the bandits on.

"You got your gun on you?" he asked Luke.

"Pffft. Of course, I do. I wouldn't not have 'em on me when I'm traveling. You didn't bring yours?"

"I didn't." Dylan didn't care for guns. He valued the one he had for protection but was not a gunslinger by any means. He would rather stab with a pen than a sword.

"We don't have time to just stand here pontificating," Luke hissed urgently. "Let's go."

## 9

Adrenaline pumped through Mattie's body as she and her brother raced down the narrow corridor toward the end of the car. At first, they heard a lot of screams and gunshots. Now, there was quiet, and that could only mean that the men were making their way through the cars, taking everything they could from the passengers. They would soon get to the car she and her brother had been riding in, and she didn't want to confront them there. The likelihood that they had Lauren with them or would take Mattie and Franklin straight to her was nonexistent.

*What have I done?* she thought frantically as Franklin yanked the door open and hopped out onto the metal connecting bridge to the next car.

He turned abruptly and grabbed her hand. "Come on. We know Trumperton is just a few miles that way. We need to go there. That's got to be where they are at. Maybe they have Lauren with them."

"Okay," Mattie agreed, letting Franklin pull her to the edge of the gangway. It looked further to the ground than Mattie thought when she'd first boarded the train and realized the platform had been just the right height to let them on the train easily. She stared down at the grassy patch below them. There were only a few feet of land before a sharp ravine going down further than she could see. There was a long gap in between where the land ended on their side to the other side many yards away.

She imagined there was a body of water running between the sides of that gap and opened her ears to hear water.

"What are you doing?" Franklin asked, staring at her, pulling on her hand. "We've got to get down there. If the bandits don't come and get us, those two men in the cabin we were in surely will."

"But it's... it's far down there, Franklin."

"It doesn't matter," he stated in a gruff voice. "Come on."

Mattie let go of his hand when he leaped

forward and plummeted toward the ground some ten or twelve feet away. To her horror, Franklin let out a sharp yell when he hit, having lost his footing immediately, and tumbled to the side. Fortunately, he didn't go as far as the ravine. Mattie hurried to get down to him, jumping but holding onto the side of the gangway rails so she wouldn't fall as he did.

She landed on her feet and knelt down to him. He was holding his arm. She was surprised, having thought he had twisted an ankle or broken a leg. The thought that they wouldn't be slowed down if it was just his arm passed through her mind and was immediately followed by guilt.

"Oh, Franklin. What happened?"

He growled, grabbing a large rock and throwing it viciously over the edge of the ravine. "Landed on that stupid rock. Argh." He was angrier than Mattie had ever seen him.

Despite the pain he must have been in, he rose to his feet and gestured with his head. His arm was limply hanging while he clutched it with the other. Mattie gazed at it, moving her eyes up to his when she spoke.

"We need to get you to a doctor. Can you move your arm? Did you break it, or is it just a bruise."

"I heard it crack. Didn't you hear it crack?"

Mattie shook her head. "No, I didn't. I'm sorry. Come on. We've got to get there as soon as we can. Maybe the sheriff there can help us."

"We can't go to the law until we know Lauren is all right. We didn't go through all of this and maybe get people killed to screw it all up by going to the law now."

Mattie ran after her brother, watching where she put her feet as she traversed the forest. According to the map she had pictured in her head, they shouldn't be too far from the town. All they had to do was make sure they were going in the same direction as the train tracks. Following them wouldn't be too hard, as long as they stayed out of sight from said tracks. Just in case the bandits got the train moving again.

She only tripped twice as she ran, and both times, she was able to right herself before she fell on her face. Franklin was still in front of her, but that was a good thing. He was making sure she didn't get tripped up by a fallen tree or large limb and that she wasn't smacked in the face by anything either.

Unfortunately, having him in the front meant that when he came out from the forest into an unexpected clearing that sharply dropped a few feet, he wasn't expecting it. Mattie stopped before she went over the side, but he didn't.

Mattie's heart fell to her stomach hearing him cry out. She imagined he was smashing his hurt arm repeatedly as his body rolled down the embankment.

"Franklin," she yelled. She only hesitated a second before going over the edge, running quickly, trying to stay on her feet as she raced after her tumbling brother. The Jack and Jill nursery rhyme went through her head. "He better not break his crown," she mumbled worriedly.

Mattie was quick on her feet. She leaped down the ravine, stretching her legs until she was in front of him. She stopped abruptly, using a tree to keep her where she was. Seconds later, when he was about to roll past her, she leaped out and grabbed him, stopping his momentum in mid-flip.

He came down on top of her and almost pulled her into his roll. But she planted her boots into the ground below her and held on for dear life.

It only took a moment or two of not rolling for Franklin to get himself righted again. But he looked like he'd been in a brawl, his face bruised and bleeding, his clothes ripped, cuts and tears all over his body.

"Oh, Franklin." Mattie couldn't help throwing herself toward him and pulling him into a tight hug. "My brother, I'm sorry. I'm sorry this happened. Now we really need to get you to the doctor. Can you walk?"

"I can walk," Franklin replied weakly, "but I can't run anymore. I think I broke a couple of toes."

Mattie's heart hurt for him. "But you *can* walk? Are you sure?"

"I'll need your help. But yeah, I think I can make it. I see a roof out there. Do you see it? That's gotta be the start of the town, don't you think? Or maybe we can get a ride into town from them. We can just say we came from the train that's being robbed. That wouldn't even be a lie."

As he talked, Mattie helped him to his feet, and they made their way down the rest of the slanted hillside. He was limping terribly, and pain was etched into the features of his face, reflecting from his eyes like a spotlight.

The roof Franklin saw turned out to be a farmhouse whose occupants were more than willing to give the two a ride into town to the clinic. The dirt road was jarring and jutted, making the brother and sister toss back and forth. Mattie held on to him as best she could without hurting his arm or crushing him. She was just trying to hold him steady.

The driver of the wagon apologized over and over, saying he was trying to hurry but not go over any rough spots. Mattie thanked him for helping them and told him not to worry about it. Soon the ride would be over, and she and her brother would be in the clinic, getting him the help he needed.

## 10

They were just outside the door of their cabin when two masked bandits came through the door of the train car. Dylan turned abruptly and yanked Luke back in the cabin just as a shot rang out.

"Thanks," Luke breathed. "Why would they shoot at me? I'm not wearing a uniform."

Dylan shook his head. "Maybe their amateurs. Come on. Help me get this window open. We'll have to go out that way."

Luke raised one brow, eyeing the window doubtfully. "We're supposed to go through that? Does it even open? Let's just shoot it out with them."

"We don't know how many there are, and I don't want to get shot."

As he spoke, Dylan went to the window and examined it. He could see how it was attached and spotted small latches along the bottom that would release the glass enough to remove it if it needed to be replaced.

"Hurry up if you're gonna open that window," Luke said nervously. "I'm surprised they haven't already come to get us."

"This train is full. They aren't coming to get us before they hit the other cabins in this car first. Come on. Help me. Just twist those latches right there." He pointed at the other side of the window. "Up the sides. Get them unlatched. Hurry up."

Luke moved into action, and soon the two had the latches undone. Dylan flattened his hands against the window and pushed it a few centimeters out. Once it was no longer on the track, Dylan and Luke jumped back as it slid from the holders and disappeared as it plummeted to the ground. The men looked at each other when they heard it crash against the rocks below and shatter.

"Be careful when you get out," Luke advised.

"A few cuts are better than being shot. Come on."

Both men crossed the room, and Dylan climbed over the sill, hanging for a moment before dropping to the ground. There was a steep ravine not far from the train tracks, but there was still plenty of room for him to safely get out.

He waited while Luke climbed out, looking to the left and the right. He could hear noise as passengers reacted to being robbed. His chest tightened as anger filled him. He felt like a coward running the way he was. As soon as Luke's boots hit the ground, Dylan gestured to him.

"Come on. I've got an idea."

Luke nodded and followed without a word as Dylan hunkered down and ran along the side of the train toward the engine.

"What's the first thing you'd do if you were robbing a stopped train?" he asked over his shoulder, not intending for Luke to answer. "You'd hit the engine first, right? Take care of the engineer, the driver. That's what I would do."

"Yeah, you're right." Luke's voice sounded like he didn't know where Dylan was going with this.

"So we need to get to the engine. Take care of the bandits that are there. Ride the train to the nearest station and get the law there to arrest these fellas."

"If any of them are still alive," Luke murmured. Dylan could hear the stress in his voice. "You know they're gonna come to the engine and try to get us."

"We'll have to fight them off. If they get shot,

that's not my problem. I didn't start this." Dylan felt a twinge of regret in his chest because he was certain Mattie and Franklin were responsible for stopping the train. They'd done it on purpose. They tried to make it seem like a coincidence.

Dylan didn't believe that for a moment.

Once they got to the engine, Dylan pulled himself up into the compartment without hesitation. He was not surprised but felt bad for the engineer, who was lying prone on the floor. He went directly to him and knelt on one knee. The man was on his side, his legs stretched out, one arm above his head, the other out in front of him. Dylan rested one hand on the man's shoulder and gently turned him over to his back. He pressed his fingers against the man's neck and waited to feel a pulse.

After a few seconds, he turned reluctant eyes to Luke, who had climbed up into the engine compartment.

"He's dead."

"Oh no," Luke murmured.

Dylan turned away from the man and looked at the gadgets, switches, levers, so many things he didn't recognize. "How are we going to get this started?"

"We'll figure it out," Luke mumbled. Dylan

watched as his friend moved to the mess of unrecognizable equipment.

"What do you see?"

Luke was about to respond when the glass of the door on the right side of the engine carriage shattered, sending shards flying through the space around the two men.

Dylan ducked initially, lifting both arms and shielding his head and face from the flying glass. Luke had turned his back and hunkered down.

There was no time to wonder what happened. A man reached in the door and unlatched the lock, opening the door. Dylan didn't waste any time.

"Get it started," he barked at Luke as he leaped toward the bandit. His first goal was to get that gun away from the outlaw. He made impact, knocking the man back toward the door. The bandit caught himself with a hand on the side of the door, still gripping his gun tight in his other hand.

Dylan ducked when the bandit swung his arm around, took quick aim, and fired at him. The bandit, whose face was covered by a kerchief, stayed where he was, astonishingly, and Dylan used that time to leap forward, both fists in front of him. He punched directly into the bandit's stomach, making the man bend in half, letting out an *oof*.

Once he was bent over, Dylan brought up his knee, connecting with the bandit's jaw and sending the man flying backward again. He landed with his head and shoulders outside the train. Just as Dylan jumped toward him, both hands extended, the train jerked into motion, the engine starting loudly with a long screeching hiss.

The outlaw let out a loud yell and jumped to his feet, tipping a little as the train began to move.

Dylan set his feet firmly so he wouldn't lose his balance with the momentum of the moving train.

"You kill this fella?" he asked, jerking one finger toward the engineer on the ground. "He probably has a family. He has friends. You took his life. You murderer."

Before the man could speak another word, Dylan closed the short distance between them, jumped up in the air, and kicked outward, his foot striking the middle of the bandit's chest. Even with the face covering, Dylan could see his eyes open wide, his hands and arms lifted up in the air as he rose into the air a couple of inches and was sent flying through the door he had left open.

Dylan ran to the door and held himself in with both hands, sticking his head out and looking in the direction the man had fallen. He was motionless on the ground. Dylan wondered if he was just unconscious or dead.

He turned around and gave Luke an impressed look. "Good job getting it started, Luke. How did you do it?"

"I'd love to say I guessed at it," Luke replied, looking sideways at Dylan, "but I was on a train as a kid, and my pa took me to explore the engine. He knew the engineer and the man explained to me everything and how it works. Basics, you know, one of them was how to start the whole thing up. Not as hard as you might think."

"I take it you know how to stop it, too?"

Luke chuckled. "If not, we can go pull an emergency cord, can't we?"

## 11

The doctor was accommodating, saying he would put Franklin's arm into a sling, and his nurse would clean up the cuts and abrasions, applying bandages where needed.

While he was being seen to, Mattie sat in the reception area of the clinic, studying her hands. The family at the farmhouse had let her wash her hands at the pump outside. The water had been so cold it stung as she ran her fingers under it. Despite her face being as dirty as it likely was, she couldn't bring herself to put the icy water on her cheeks. She would have to remain dirty until she could find warmer water.

Her fingers hurt. Everything about her hurt. All

she wanted to do was go home and lay in her bed after taking a nice long hot bath.

The way it looked at that moment, it was going to be a long time before she got her wish.

The nurse came out of the room her brother was in and gave her a smile but didn't say anything. She hurried down the short hallway to a door, which she pulled open. While Mattie looked on, the nurse pulled supplies from the stock in the closet. She recognized the sling when the nurse took it out, adding it to the handful of bandages she was holding.

She closed the door and returned to the room, once again giving Mattie a warm smile, which Mattie returned.

Her mind was racing with thoughts of despair. The gunshot they'd heard rang in her mind over and over. What if the person who had been shot was dead? Was she responsible for that death?

Chills covered her body, and her eyes stung with tears. She *was* responsible. She knew it. She had stopped the train. Well, technically, Franklin had, but that wasn't the point. It was because of her. It was because of Lauren. They were all as guilty of the murder as the man who had shot his gun.

Her tears came faster than she thought they

would, and she had to lower her head quickly and cover her eyes with one hand. Sobs racked her body. Someone had likely died, and she still didn't have her sister back. What if Lauren was already dead, too?

A sharp knife stabbed Mattie in the heart.

Lauren was *not* dead. She would *not* allow herself to think that way.

The two men in the cabin she and Franklin had occupied slipped into her mind and stayed her tears, distracting her. The one named Dylan had been quite a man to reckon with. He and his chauvinistic views. She felt a bit of anger fill her chest, which was a relief from the pain of grief and guilt she was feeling. She would rather be angry at the man for his disgusting views than feel the weight of the tremendous guilt from what she'd done.

Despite the way he talked, he had impressed her. And when they had returned, he *had* apologized, hadn't he? It didn't take much for Mattie to forgive. She might be angry about it again later, but she had to admit, it took quite a man to even apologize in the first place.

And he had been devilishly good-looking, hadn't he?

Mattie's tears had stopped. She was looking at

Dylan in her mind, thinking about his awful words and then his apology. His friend hadn't been nearly as intriguing. The funny thing was, Mattie felt more interest in Dylan—the one with such awful views on women—than Luke, who clearly didn't feel those things. Or at least not as strongly as Dylan did.

She kneaded her fingers together, pulling on them, stretching them. Everything hurt. Her heart, her brain, her head, her body. It all hurt.

Thinking about Dylan somehow eased her pain. Was it because he distracted her from it? Or was it something deeper than that?

The door to the room Franklin was in opened once more, and the nurse came out. She was followed by Franklin, his arm in the sling the doctor had provided, his face clean, showing where he'd been scratched up in his fall. He'd been provided new clothes, and Mattie was left wondering how she'd missed seeing the nurse fetch them and how they fit her brother so well.

She stood up and approached, her arms out to take him into a hug, which he received with a gentle smile and one hand around her waist.

"There you are," she said quietly into his ear. She pulled back and looked into his similar hazel eyes.

"Are you all right? Was nothing broken? Do you remember me? Can you still count to ten?"

As she asked her inane questions, a smile grew on his face, which is what she was looking for. He chuckled softly and shook his head. "Surprisingly, I didn't hit my head once on the way down that ravine." He lifted his good hand and knocked his knuckles lightly against the side of his head above his ear. "Still pretty sound," he said.

"Well, good," Mattie replied firmly, "because I need my brother to help me through this trial we're going through. So you be a little more careful with yourself."

"I was trying to be careful, to begin with," he stated sardonically.

Mattie put her arm around him, and they walked to the reception desk, where the nurse had taken a seat.

"The charge is two dollars," the nurse said, checking her chart and jotting down a receipt for Mattie. She handed it to her without another word.

Mattie took it and looked down at it. "I haven't paid you yet." Her voice was questioning.

"It's all right. We can afford to let you have the sling. And we weren't seeing anyone else, so it was good timing for an emergency."

"I don't know how you'll stay in practice that way," Mattie replied. "We should pay you what we owe you." She glanced behind her at the bag she'd left at the chair she'd been sitting in. Her eyes moved abruptly to her hand when the nurse stood up suddenly and took it in both of hers, surrounding the receipt as well. The woman used one hand to press the receipt into Mattie's.

"You two go on and finish your task. Your brother was a little drowsy from the medication we gave him. He will be drowsy for a few hours, I suspect. It is to help with the pain. His arm is fractured. While he was drowsy, he told the doctor and me what you two are going through. We do hope you find your sister. Soon."

Mattie stood there, frozen in place, her eyes staring at the nurse. She glanced at her brother, whose head was down, his eyes closed. Fear seized her heart, and she squeezed him with the arm she still had around him. "Franklin?"

His eyes snapped open, and he looked at her. "I'm okay, Mattie," he said. "Just tired."

Worry filled Mattie's mind. There was nowhere they could go for him to rest. What were they to do?

The sound of the train rumbling into the station outside made all three of them turn to look at the window, which was rattling. Chills covered Mattie from head to toe. She shared a wide-eyed glance with her brother, who, through his dazed state, was aware that something unexpected had just happened.

"We... we have to go."

"Wait. Take these." The nurse ran from the reception room to the closet Mattie had seen her take the sling from. She yanked the door open and began to grab items. When she returned just seconds later, she was carrying a large sack with a handle. "Blankets, extra bandages, some cleaning supplies for you. I don't have any food, I'm sorry. We hope you find your sister. Good luck and Godspeed."

Without a second thought, Mattie grabbed the bag from her. Panic had set in, and all she could think about was getting Franklin to a safe place. "Thank you so much for everything. Come on, Franklin."

## 12

As soon as the train pulled into the station, Dylan and Luke jumped from the engine. Luke had pulled the brakes long before they got to the station, knowing it took at least half a mile to slow to a stop. As they ran through the woods, they heard the people on the train running from it, causing a loud scene in the street.

"Come on." Dylan tapped Luke on the chest, and the two ran through the woods away from the train.

"Where are we going?"

"We need to stay hidden until the sheriff goes and arrests those bandits. I don't want them running after us either."

"The law? Why would they come after us?"

"Not the law, Luke," Dylan retorted shortly. "The bandits. I don't want them seeing us and coming after us. They're gonna run from the train, obviously. Don't want them seeing us."

They were well away from the train by that point. Dylan sent several glances over his shoulder toward the great locomotive but didn't see anyone who looked suspicious. He wondered if the bandits had removed their face coverings and joined the crowd.

Their clothes were unmistakable, though. In such a traumatizing situation, it was unlikely none of the passengers would recognize them by their clothes.

Dylan was going to leave that up to the other passengers. He wasn't sticking around. He and Luke had made them upset by starting the train and getting it back in motion. Of that, he had no doubt. The only one who had seen them both, though, was the one who'd jumped into the engine car. He couldn't be sure the ones that had entered the car they'd been in originally had seen either him or Luke.

Either way, he didn't want to get caught up in it. He wasn't a fighting man. He wasn't a gunslinger. It had nothing to do with cowardice. He just didn't want to die or get shot.

They were almost to the edge of the town and could see the first building nearing when Dylan slid to a sudden halt. He put out his hand and stopped Luke in his tracks, as well. Luke gave him a curious look and followed Dylan's gaze.

"Well, well, well," Dylan said under his breath. Ahead of them, some thirty or thirty-five yards, almost hidden in the brush, were Mattie and Franklin, sitting together under a shade tree. He couldn't see them clearly but recognized the hooded cape Mattie was wearing. It was the color of bronze and unmistakable.

"We should just leave them alone," Luke remarked.

Dylan slid his eyes to his friend. "They got us into this trouble," he pointed out. "If he hadn't pulled that cord, the bandits wouldn't have gotten on the train at all. No way could they have stopped it by themselves. She helped them."

"You think they did it on purpose?" Luke asked, doubt in his voice. "It looked like a genuine act to me. And they don't look like bandits to me."

"Who *looks* like an outlaw?" Dylan questioned. "Come on. I want to find out."

"Why?" Luke persisted. "We should just leave them alone."

Dylan shook his head, determined to find out more about that woman. She was intriguing. She seemed so strong and adventurous and courageous. He was sure he'd never met a woman like her before. He had to know if she was on the wrong side of the law. It would nag at his mind if he never found out.

He hurried in their direction, trying to stay behind trees so he wouldn't be seen until he was much closer. He could hear Luke grumbling behind him and sent a narrow look over his shoulder at his friend.

Dylan came up behind the two and stopped, surprised they hadn't turned to him yet.

He cleared his throat, and still, they didn't turn. Pulling his eyebrows together and giving Luke a curious glance, which was returned by his friend along with a shrug of shoulders, Dylan said, "Mattie? Franklin?"

Both the siblings spun around and looked up at him and Luke, shock etched on their faces.

"Oh," Mattie cried out softly, relief in her voice and on her face. "It's you. Thank you, Lord. We thought you were the bandits."

Dylan pulled back a little and stared at her. "Okay, I'll need you to please explain yourself." He came around to look at them both from the front and knelt on one knee, staring at Mattie. "I've been trying to convince myself you weren't working with the thieves, but that comment makes me think maybe you were. What's going on? Do we need to take you to the sheriff? Are you working with those men?"

He turned his eyes to Franklin, who looked like he'd been in a fist fight with a thorny bush. He certainly didn't look like he was an outlaw. He looked like he needed to be behind a desk somewhere calculating numbers.

"Surely you two aren't bandits yourselves," he said, shaking his head. "You just don't have the look."

"Well, I'm surely glad to know that opinion of us, sir," Mattie huffed. "And I'd like to know how you know my name."

Dylan lifted one eyebrow. He tapped one of his ears. "I can hear. I heard him call you Mattie." He pointed at Franklin and then at her. "And I heard you call him Franklin. So now I know your names."

"He is Frederick to you," Mattie said firmly. "We don't know you. You can't call him by a familiar name."

Dylan tried not to show his amusement on his face. "All right. I'll agree to that if you tell me why you helped those outlaws. The more I look at the two of you, the more I think it might actually have been a coincidence. Then again, you said something about them coming to find you. So what is it? Do we need to haul you two to the sheriff or not?"

"No," Franklin spoke up. When he continued, his words came out in a rush, and Dylan found himself feeling sorry for the younger man. "We didn't do anything wrong... I mean, we... we did but only because those men have our sister. Our sister, Lauren. They took her, and they are making us do things to help them so we can get her back."

Dylan frowned. "Your sister has been kidnapped? By the outlaws that held up the train?" He didn't really need confirmation of those two facts. He already believed Franklin one hundred percent.

"Yes, that's right," Mattie gushed, her words coming out as quickly as her brother's had. "Our father had a party, and she was taken from there, and we just want her back. We don't want anyone hurt or killed. I didn't know they were going to shoot anyone. They did, didn't they?"

Mattie seemed to deflate right in front of him. Her shoulders slumped, tears sprang to her eyes, she lowered her head. The dead engineer came to Dylan's mind, but he said nothing.

"Don't worry about that right now. Luke and I

will go get a couple of rooms for the night. Let's all get something to eat and relax for tonight and try to figure out what to do in the morning. There's nothing you can do at this moment, anyway, is there?"

Mattie clenched her jaw. He could see it flex. She nodded, though, leaving her determined eyes on him.

"All right," she said.

"You can stay in the rooms with us," Dylan added. "So you will be safe. Nothing will happen to either of you while Luke and I are around."

He was pleased with the relieved look on the young woman's face. It made her look even more radiant and attractive.

## 13

Mattie listened as Franklin talked to Luke in low tones about an interest they discovered they both shared—medicine. Franklin had dreamed of becoming a doctor since he was a child. It was his goal in life. Apparently, Luke had trained under a doctor and was able to discuss the topic with a broad range of knowledge.

She was pleased something had come up to distract Franklin from his pain. It was distressing to her that he even had to feel it. If she could, she would have taken it from him.

"Penny for your thoughts?"

The man named Dylan Sullivan, who had helped her and Franklin out of the woods safely, was seated next to her on her right at the table in the restaurant. Her stomach was growling, and she was waiting anxiously for the beef stew she could smell cooking in the back kitchen. She was devouring the rolls that had been placed in the middle of the table, not even bothering to butter them.

She glanced at him quickly before returning her eyes to her hands as she pulled pieces of bread from the roll and stuffed them in her mouth. "Hungry," she said, the corners of her lips twitching with humor.

"You are eating quite voraciously," Dylan remarked.

She stopped for only a moment to give him a wide-eyed stare. "Big words," she stated.

He chuckled. "When was the last time you ate, though? You really do look like you've been—"

"I ate this morning," she interrupted him. "I'm eating like this because I'm terribly nervous, and yes, it's been a few hours. It's lunchtime. I should be hungry."

"That hungry?" he persisted. "You sure you haven't been starving for a long time now? I can get you some food if you need it. A place to stay, no problem. Where did you start your journey?"

Mattie had resumed eating but stopped again

when she realized he had no idea who she was. There was really no reason for him to know who she was. They were complete strangers. Doubtful he'd ever been to Bighorn other than to pass through on his way wherever he was going on the train.

"I, uh, I don't need those things," she responded, knowing her words were coming out sounding a little idiotic. "We, uh," She looked at her brother, who wasn't paying any attention to them whatsoever. "We are fine," she continued, wondering if she should reveal who she was. If these two men realized she and Franklin were the children of a well-known Texas judge, what would they do? Would they see dollar signs in their eyes and ransom the two of them off themselves?

And what would that do to Lauren? How would they find her and rescue her if they themselves had become kidnap victims?

When Mattie looked at Dylan, she wanted to trust him. She felt like she could see the trust in his eyes. But that edge of doubt nagging at the back of her mind kept her from revealing who she was.

"You don't need to worry about us," she stated firmly. "My brother and I will be just fine, thank you."

Dylan hesitated a moment before nodding and

sitting back, taking his eyes from her. It almost felt cold to her without his gaze upon her, but she was sure that was just in her mind.

"Well, all right then. I like to be of assistance to people in need, that's all. I don't mind helping a damsel in distress and her brother when I can."

Mattie bristled at his phrase damsel in distress. She was no damsel, and she wasn't in distress. Sure, she felt guilty for her part in the robbery and even felt some guilt that it was her sister who had been taken and not her. If it had been her, she would have fought back. They would have met their match with her.

Perhaps that's why they took Lauren in the first place. Or maybe, as she and Franklin had discussed, Lauren knew them and had gone along with their plan.

Either way, Mattie was guilty of so much. Being labeled a victim in the situation raised her ire.

She stood up, dropping the remainder of the roll in her hand on her plate. "I need some fresh air," she snapped. She looked at Dylan's bewildered face before lowering her eyes to the plate, reaching down, and snatching her roll. "I will be outside until more food comes."

She turned on one heel and sauntered toward

the door, going out on the walkway and standing there, breathing slowly.

To her right was a fruit stand, offering such a beautiful-looking variety when Mattie was terribly hungry that she could barely contain herself from picking up something. To her left was the newspaper stand.

To her horror, when she looked at the front page of the *Babylon Times*, imported from the larger city nearby, she saw something that sent chills down her spine.

It was a picture of her entire family. Splashed in black and white across the front of the newspaper were the words *"Children of beloved Judge Carter Holbrook discovered missing."*

Bile rose up in Mattie's throat, and she put one hand over her mouth, repeatedly swallowing to keep it down. She turned around and was about to run back into the restaurant when she nearly ran head-first into Dylan, who was just stepping out through the door.

"Oh," she cried, stepping back, her eyes lifted and taking in his handsome face. His lips settled into an easy grin.

"Whoa, whoa, there," he said with a soft laugh. "You move way too much, Mattie, you know that? Or must I call you Matilda? Or whatever your given name is."

"Mattie is fine," she snapped and instantly regretted saying it like that. She eased her tone and relaxed her shoulders, letting out her breath through her nose quietly. "I'm sorry. I'm so on edge. I just can't help myself." She stepped to the left and leaned on the booth where the newspapers were, lifting one hand and placing the back of it on her forehead. "I thought the fresh air would help me calm down."

While he looked on, she positioned herself perfectly to stand in front of the newspaper so he wouldn't see it.

"I'm sorry this is all happening to you, Mattie. I want to help you. I don't want to push you away."

Mattie stared at him now, tilting her head to the side and blinking. "Push me away? You barely know me, yet you use words that only a beau would say to his sweetheart."

To her astonishment, his face flushed, and he looked away, stammering, "I... that wasn't exactly... I'm only trying to..."

Mattie felt a rush of amusement. Without her permission, her face softened, and she smiled at him. "It's all right. I'm the one who should be apologizing to you. I don't know what's come over me. I'm usually not this rude. Let's go back inside and talk. My brother and Luke don't seem to be having any trouble getting along. Why shouldn't we get along like that, too?"

She saw the pleased look he was giving her, and it sent a nice tingle up her spine. Her thighs lit on fire when she brushed past him to go back inside. He'd stepped to the side but not so far that they would not touch when she went by.

Mattie told herself he did that on purpose. He could have stepped back more.

The next moment, she was wondering why she was thinking such intimate thoughts about him.

## 14

D

ylan, on the other hand, knew exactly what he was feeling and why. The woman was incredibly intriguing. After they'd filled their stomachs, they were all showing signs of fatigue and decided to retire to the boarding house room they had rented for the night. They each got their own room, which thrilled the boarding house manager.

Dylan had left them in his room to get something for them all to drink and was now heading back with a bottle of whiskey and a bottle of sweet brandy. He had no idea what kind of drink Mattie would like or even if she drank. Therefore, it stood to reason he should get two opposing styles, and she could have her choice. For some reason, he didn't see her as the whiskey-drinking type. Usually, when he encountered a woman who wanted to be independent and sit at the table with the men, she was rough around the edges, generally not attractive in the face and even less attractive in personality.

Mattie was none of those things. He could picture her coming from a nice family with a decent, small home, with loving parents who were there for them at all times.

His imagination didn't follow the facts, though, and he knew his assessment of her home life was probably pretty far off. If her sister was kidnapped and held while the siblings did their bidding, they were more likely to be from a family of influence. The stakes would be higher in that situation than for an average family. In addition, Franklin's conversations with Luke indicated he had a background, an education that had served him well. Dylan wouldn't be at all surprised if Mattie was equally well educated but on different topics than her brother.

He passed the restaurant again and glanced inside. It was packed full of people from the train that had yet to take off again, probably because the engineer was dead. He saw a variety of looks on the stranded passengers' faces. Some seemed content and were eating with pleasure, talking to their companions, who responded amiably. Some looked distraught and worried, while others looked simply angry. It had to be frustrating to be caught somewhere when you were on your way to a destination for a reason. No one traveled without a reason.

His eyes dropped to the newspapers stacked in front of the stand, and he felt a cold chill race over his body. He stopped and stared at the paper.

It was a photograph of a family of five. Two younger woman and a younger man. Two parents. One of them, a judge. The other was a prominent member of a prestigious family.

It was the Holbrooks. Judge Carter Sage Holbrook, his wife, Abigail, their three children, Mattie, Franklin, and Lauren.

Dylan fished in his pocket for a coin, which he handed the boy behind the booth.

"Thanks," the boy said, flashing a toothy grin.

Dylan just nodded, his eyes still on the paper, which he picked up. He unfolded it and read the article, his skin crawling the longer he read.

*In the late afternoon hours, Judge Holbrook and his wife discovered all three of their children missing from their home with no explanation. It appears Miss Lauren Holbrook's bed had not been slept in, and although her siblings did appear to be in the home all night and were there for breakfast, they are nowhere to be found at this time. Reports say they were last seen going toward the train station, but Judge Holbrook and his wife deny their children were taking a trip. Anyone with information about the missing children should contact their local sheriff, who will get in touch with the proper authorities.*

Dylan was amazed at how quickly the news had spread. However, it left him with questions. Why had the children decided not to tell their parents? Why hadn't they left a message for them, a note saying they were somewhere else? They hadn't covered their tracks very well at all. He also wondered how much communication Mattie and Franklin really had with the actual kidnappers. How did they know where to stop the train? How were they communicating with the outlaws?

He continued on to the boarding house, which was just up the road another block. He finished the article on the way and left the paper on a bench outside the barber shop for someone else to find.

By the time he got to the boarding house, he'd decided he wasn't going to say anything to Mattie about seeing the newspaper and knowing who she was. He could tell it made her uncomfortable for him to know the truth, and even though he didn't know why she would want to keep that from him, he wasn't going to question her motives. They were hers to decide, and he had nothing to do with it.

Luke and Franklin were having a good conversation when he entered the room. He could tell it was amiable and friendly by the look on Mattie's face, and she wasn't even involved in it. She was sitting in one of the chairs by the window, glancing up at her brother and his new friend with a secret smile on her face.

All three turned their heads to gaze at him. "There's my best friend," Luke said abruptly, jumping to his feet. Dylan lifted his eyebrows as Luke crossed the room and snatched the bottle of whiskey from him. He gazed at it lovingly, and the other three laughed when he said, "There you are, my beautiful bottle of whiskey. Thanks, fella." He said the last part to Dylan and slapped one hand on his shoulder.

Dylan snorted in response. He turned his eyes to Mattie, who was gazing at him. "You like whiskey or sweet brandy?"

"Brandy, please," Mattie responded, giving him the satisfaction that he had guessed right.

"I think the whiskey will be good for Franklin," Dylan continued, getting four glasses from a small cupboard hanging on the wall. He poured the brandy in a glass for her while Luke filled the other three with whiskey. He was amused by the fact that Luke hadn't asked Franklin if he wanted the whiskey. He simply poured it regardless.

Dylan took one of the whiskey glasses and Mattie's glass, handing it to her when he crossed the room and sat down. She was in a chair that was sitting at an angle to him. She was closer to the window, but it was at her side, so she could see straight through it. There was a white table between the two angled chairs, and Dylan set his whiskey glass on it, not really interested in drinking quite yet.

Mattie, however, took a sip of her brandy and nodded at him. "This is very sweet brandy. I like it. Thank you so much."

Dylan nodded back. "You're welcome. Glad you like it."

He settled into the chair. He couldn't help gazing at her face. Now that he knew something about her that she didn't know he knew, he felt special. Like he had something on her. He wouldn't use it for nefarious purposes, but she was such a formidable character, he couldn't help feeling a bit of pride that he knew what he knew.

"So, tell me," Mattie said, seeming to relax a bit,

"what do you do when you aren't rescuing ladies and their brothers from the clutches of outlaws?"

He smiled at her. "That's just my regular job, I guess. It happens all the time."

She pouted in a pretty manner, pushing out her lower lip slightly. "Oh, and I thought I was special."

You're definitely special, he thought before saying. "You are. I'm just teasing. This literally never happens to me. I run an advertising company in Bighorn, Texas, and I'm looking to start a magazine of my own. Well, Luke and I. That's the goal."

## 15

The conversation from the train ran through her mind. Mattie nodded, looking at him. "That's right. You said that on the train, didn't you?"

He looked nervous. "Yes, that's right."

"The gentleman's magazine."

She took another sip of her brandy, looking at him over the rim, knowing her stare was making him uncomfortable. He shifted in his seat in a cute way, and Mattie had to fight the smile from bursting from her lips.

"Yes," he said again. "That's right."

She tilted her head to the side, wondering why he was suddenly so reluctant about the topic. He had been more than willing to talk about it in front of her while they were in the train car. What had changed since then?

She wondered if he was being condescending. Maybe he just looked uncomfortable and was avoiding the topic because he didn't want her getting upset.

Mattie's thoughts fought inside her mind.

"Tell me, what makes you think the way you do?"

She'd thought he would be confused about what she meant, but when his jaw moved and his eyes roamed the room, she knew he was thinking about the best way to put it. He understood what she meant by her question. She was glad he didn't play stupid.

"In my experience," he began, his voice even and smooth, "any woman that has been put in a dire situation has failed to live up to expectations. Women think emotionally and can't handle the pressure of some of the things men have to deal with. It's just better if women left the running of things to the men."

Mattie held in her shock. Why should she be shocked? She already knew he felt that way.

But even as he spoke, she heard what she thought was a small amount of doubt. Would it be possible for him to change his mind? Would she be the one to make him change it?

She had to admit, he was good-looking, intelligent, and he owned a business. He was definitely the kind of man her father would like. There would be no trouble there if they decided to court.

She mentally shook her head to clear her thoughts away. What kind of woman is attracted to a man with such chauvinistic views?

Her, apparently. She was that kind of woman. What if she was just trying to change him? Her mother had said men couldn't be changed. She would have to accept her beau for all his flaws and faults, along with his redeeming qualities.

Mattie wasn't sure she wouldn't mind accepting Dylan's flaws.

"Women are just as capable as men. My mother runs several clubs and handles the finances for women who don't know how to do that kind of thing. She helps the widows continue making money and provide for their children. She knows how to run a household. And have you ever had a housekeeper? They run the house for many men, making sure everything is running smoothly."

"There are women who are capable of doing that," Dylan admitted, giving her a bit of satisfaction, "but the majority aren't capable. My father taught me that women are emotional creatures. Nothing they do can be done without involving their emotions. And when they shouldn't be taken into account, you do anyway. Not you, of course. Just women. Women take things to heart. They take everything personally and then set out for revenge if they don't get what they want."

"My goodness," Mattie exclaimed, shaking her head. "Did you have a mother growing up? Didn't she show you any love?"

"My mother died when I was very young," Dylan confessed. He glanced at Luke, and Mattie wondered why. "I didn't really have many women around when I was growing up. And my father taught me everything I know about that topic."

Mattie felt the need to sit forward, folding one leg underneath the other as she set her cup on the table between them.

"Listen, Dylan, you have a lot to learn about women. We have many layers, and one of them is emotional. That is true. But the other layers consist of things like compassion, common sense, intelligence, and understanding. Emotion always plays some kind of role, even with men, you have to admit that. Lack of emotion when making decisions could affect the outcome in a negative way. If not the outcome, then the people affected by it."

Dylan held her gaze, and she was thrilled by it. She had his full attention.

"I can show you how a real woman acts in the face of turmoil. I have made decisions that have had good outcomes and some that have bad outcomes. But it's the same for men. Men are layered, too. And I think those layers are different, not only between men and women but between every single individual and everyone else. No one is exactly the same on the outside or the inside. Even when you find someone you have a lot in common with, there will still always be differences, whether you like strawberries when they don't or something like that."

Dylan chuckled, making Mattie's heart thump harder in her chest. His smile was dazzling, whether it was small or stretched from ear to ear.

"You're right," he conceded.

Mattie grinned at him. "You aren't as hardheaded as I initially thought you were."

"If I change my views on women," he stated, "what in heaven's name will my magazine be about?"

Mattie raised her eyebrows. "Surely you haven't already changed them. That didn't take very much.

You must not have been a firm believer in how awful women are at running things."

He laughed, this time sending a delighted thrill through Mattie, making her heart pound and her blood race. "I haven't given up on my convictions just yet," he replied in a sly voice, "but you might be making me see from a broader picture, and there's nothing wrong with that, is there?"

"Not at all," she said. "Not at all."

"The sun will be going down in a few hours," Dylan remarked. "I suppose you want to just stay in here until morning?"

"Actually, I'd like to go for a walk before it gets dark. I'm curious to know if those bandits are in the jail or not. I don't see why I can't just ask the sheriff, you know? He would tell me. I was a passenger on that train, too, wasn't I?"

"You certainly were," Dylan replied with a nod.

"You aren't going anywhere alone," Franklin stated firmly from his seat on the bed. One leg was pulled up beside him, and he was holding his half-empty whiskey glass between both hands. "I'll go with you. We have to be careful. If those bandits aren't in jail, they will be looking for us."

"I think they're more likely to have taken off,"

Luke put in. "No way would they stick around. They will be gone by now."

Mattie looked at the man, realizing he had not heard her tell Dylan about their situation with Lauren. She turned her eyes to Dylan and raised her eyebrows.

"I'll fill him in while you two are gone," Dylan said helpfully. "We're looking forward to hearing your report."

Mattie couldn't help thinking that was a strange thing to say, but she nodded. "Of course, I will," she responded. She finished off the sweet brandy, which had made her head float just a little, and pushed to her feet.

"Let's go now. I don't want to be out there when it's dark."

"You got that right."

They said goodbye to their companions. Mattie would have sworn she could feel Dylan's eyes boring a hole in her back as they left the room.

## 16

As soon as they were outside the door to Dylan's room, Franklin grabbed his sister's hand and hurried away from it. She raised her eyebrows and gave him a curious look. He might have been two years younger, but he was taller than she was, and she had to take quick steps to keep up with his long legs.

"What are you doing, Franklin? We don't have to hurry."

"It's been a couple of hours, Mattie," her brother responded. "I think things will have calmed down by now, don't you?"

She nodded, coming up beside him after pulling her hand from his. "Yeah, I do. That's why I don't know why you're yanking on me like that. We don't have to hurry."

"I just wanted to get away from the door, so we could talk, that's all," he finally admitted.

Mattie tossed a look over her shoulder to the end of the hallway, where the door to the room they'd just left remained closed.

"Well, they aren't following us or trying to listen in or see where we're going. What are you so worried about?"

"I'm not worried," Franklin insisted. "I'm just thinking. I like them and all, but can we trust them, really?"

Mattie was bewildered. The entire time, she'd been thinking Franklin was getting along well with Luke and that he had no problem with Dylan. "Well..." She hesitated before continuing, "I kind of had those feelings, too, wondering if we can trust them or not. But I don't think we really have a choice right now. They know that we stopped that train. Someone could have died because we stopped it, and that would be terrible."

"We only did it for Lauren, Mattie. And now I'm really worried that they are gonna kill her because they were caught."

"We don't even know how many there are in that

gang. We don't know where she is or if she's alive. We don't know anything." The frustration of it all came over Mattie all at once, and she felt a sweep of anger rush through her. It left her feeling weak, knowing that her anger could do nothing to help find her sister. "Let's just get to the sheriff and find out what happened."

Neither spoke another word as they headed toward the bustling sheriff's office inside the jailhouse. People were gathered around outside, talking to each other. Mattie saw many upset faces. She opened her ears to the conversations around her as she and Franklin went through the crowd.

"I can't believe we still have to wait here. This is taking forever. We will be late for the wedding at this rate."

"How can it take so long to replace an engineer? Doesn't anyone local know how to drive that thing?"

"I've never been so delayed in all my life. Especially in a one-horse town like this."

Mattie went up the steps, wondering why they had to replace the engineer. She had a feeling she knew what that meant but wouldn't allow herself to believe it until she heard it from the sheriff. Her chest tightened around her heart, an internal vice squeezing her heart.

The sheriff and two deputies were handling the remainder of the people from the train. The passengers were wandering around the area, gazing at what was left of the loot the robbers had taken from them.

"I swear if I don't see my brooch soon, I'll go out there and find it amongst those ladies. One of them will have it. I know it."

"No one stole your brooch, Mama," the young woman beside her said softly. "I'm sure it's here somewhere. Look, over there. Isn't that it?"

"Why, yes, it is. Thank goodness. I did not want to confront any of them for being a thief."

"You're silly, mama. Come on, let's go eat while we wait for the train people to send another engineer."

The older woman clucked her teeth. "So sad about that poor man. I didn't know him, but I'll pray for his family."

"Me, too, Mama. Me, too."

The women moved out from behind Mattie to leave the jailhouse.

Mattie's heart had plummeted to her stomach when her worst fears were confirmed.

Someone had died.

They had actually killed someone.

"May I help you?"

A deputy had come over to them and raised his eyebrows, making his narrow face look hawk-like.

"Yes, uh, we were passengers on the train," Franklin said, stammering slightly. "We, uh, want to know what happened to the bandits. Did you catch them?"

"We caught two of 'em." The deputy, whose nametag said "Sinclair," lifted his belt and pants, rocking back on his heels. "I think there are more. They won't own up to it, but I'm bettin' you there are plenty more of 'em, and we need to be out there scouring the woods to find 'em. Thinkin' about puttin' together a posse. Don't you worry, little lass." He grinned and winked at Mattie, who felt slightly sick to her stomach. "We're gonna find 'em. We'll catch 'em and lock 'em up. Don't worry your pretty little head."

Mattie nodded and smiled graciously. "That's wonderful. Thank you, Deputy Sinclair."

"You just go ahead and find whatever is yours and go on out to wait for the new engineer."

Mattie's eyebrows pulled together as she thought about the man who had been driving the train.

"About that... how did it happen? Do you know?"

"Looks like he was hit on the head with something hard. Maybe hit it on the way down. No bullet wound. Them boys in there say they just scared him, shootin' in the air, and he tripped back and hit his head. That's consistent with what looked like might have happened. But it was hard to tell because he was on his back when we got on."

"How did the train even get to Trumperton?" Franklin asked. "When they... when they stopped the train, we were down about five miles or so, I think. How did it get here?"

"Folks around town say they saw a couple of men jump from the engine and run off into the woods.

Mattie's skin erupted in tingles. "Two men? What did they look like?"

"Didn't get a description, but they weren't wearing kerchiefs, and the passengers are sayin' the men who robbed it were wearing kerchiefs." He shook his head. "A durn shame we couldn't catch those two. They might know something. But that's lookin' for a needle in a haystack, I must say."

"Thank you, Deputy Sinclair, for everything. Come on, Franklin." She pulled on her brother's hand and hurried back toward the door.

"Dontcha want to get your stuff that was stolen?" the deputy called after them.

She glanced over her shoulder at him. "We'll get it later on."

"But... but—"

The door slammed behind them, and Mattie rushed to get down the steps and around to the side of the building. She'd taken to carrying a sack of supplies she might need hanging from the waist band of any dress she was wearing. She wouldn't admit it to anyone, but she'd found there was great comfort and convenience to wearing men's pants.

As she went around the building and hurried down the alleyway with her brother right behind her, Mattie pulled the sack up into her hands and untied it. She pulled out a small notepad and a pen.

"What are you doing?"

"We have to get a note to them. We have to talk to them."

"What good is your paper going to do if we don't know which cell they are in. If you write a note and put it in the wrong cell, we'll be in a whole lot of trouble."

"That's not going to happen," Mattie answered him, practically under her breath.

There were four windows along the back of the jail. They were high up, higher than she could reach, but she was positive she could fold the paper down small and toss it over.

## 17

Dylan watched Luke sleeping. He must have been completely exhausted to fall asleep as fast as he did. Dylan couldn't feel it coming. Luke had fallen asleep on his bed, and if he wasn't awake when Dylan returned from the outing he was about to take, he would simply take Luke's bed and room. It wasn't a big thing to switch.

As soon as the siblings left his room, he'd gotten up and gone to the window. He stayed that way until he saw Mattie and Franklin come out of the boarding house and head down the street. They stopped a few times and talked, Mattie waving her hands around. Franklin did nothing but nod.

Dylan wondered if the brother and sister ever

fought. They cared tremendously for each other. That much was obvious.

When he saw them skirt through the crowd outside the jailhouse and go in, he passed his sleeping friend and went out the door himself.

Dylan left the boarding house, pulling a cigarette he'd rolled from his front pocket and a box of matches from another.

He stood where he was, just outside the boarding house, smoking the cigarette and blowing curling smoke through the air in front of him.

He remained highly impressed with Mattie. It was almost amusing how strong he was in his convictions before he met her. Women definitely had a place in society, and men were above them in rank. They were there to take care of their men and children, to clean and cook and run a household—nothing else. Men were the only ones capable of making sound decisions that wouldn't jeopardize everyone and everything around them.

That's what he'd thought.

It had only taken Mattie a few hours to dismantle what he'd previously believed. He had no doubt in his mind that Mattie was capable of doing whatever she put her mind to. He knew men who wouldn't do the brave things Mattie had already shown the ability to do.

Dylan's eyes narrowed suddenly and not because the smoke was in his face as he drew a hit from the cigarette.

Mattie and Franklin had reappeared. They were skirting down the steps and going around the jailhouse to the alleyway where they disappeared.

Intensely curious about what the two were doing, Dylan sprinted quickly across the road, making sure the way was clear before going. He speed-walked down the walkway until he reached the alley he'd seen the two go into. None of the people lingering outside the place were looking at him. He went completely unnoticed, just like the siblings. Everyone else had their own troubles on their minds, namely, how they were going to get out of this godforsaken, one-horse town as soon as possible. At least, that's what he heard as he passed them by.

Mattie and Franklin weren't in the alleyway. Dylan hurried to the end of it, where the buildings on both sides of him stopped. He didn't go immediately out into the dirt road that ran along the backs of the buildings on that street.

Instead, he pressed himself against the exterior

wall and moved very slowly until he was at the corner. He peeked around and saw something he never expected to see. It was so unexpected he had to jerk back, push himself flat against the wall, and slap one hand over his mouth so he wouldn't let out a laugh.

Mattie was balancing on her brother's shoulders, staring into one of the windows, her hands clutching the bars that flanked her slender face.

Dylan waited a minute, heard one of the siblings hissing words he couldn't understand and a bit of shuffling. He peeked around again and saw Mattie writing frantically on a piece of paper in a small notepad. He'd wondered what that sack attached to her waist was for. He, too, had a notepad and a pen on his person. But he was a writer, and that's what writers did.

He peeked around once more and watched as Mattie finished the note, ripped it from her notepad, folded it several times, and stood back from the exterior of the cell. She took aim and tossed the note. It bounced off one of the bars and came back to her. She caught it neatly in her hands.

"Try again," Franklin whispered loudly, encouraging her. Dylan liked that. He liked the kid a lot.

Just another reason to stick with Mattie. He wanted to make sure they were both safe.

Mattie did try again, and this time, it zipped right between the bars. Dylan waited as anxiously as Franklin and Mattie.

"Hey, he probably doesn't have anything to write back with," Franklin murmured. "Throw the pen over."

"But this is my only good pen," Mattie replied in haste.

Dylan nearly gave himself away and had to once again hold in a laugh.

"He'll throw it back," Franklin responded, his voice an octave higher than usual.

Dylan bent over, laughing silently into his hand.

Mattie made a sound of great frustration, and Dylan had to squeeze his lips shut. He peeked around and saw her toss the pen through the window.

His eyes moved up to the window, and they all waited. Less than a minute later, the paper came flying back out, and the pen followed shortly after.

"What's it say? What's it say?" Franklin sounded anxious.

"Hold on a minute, Lord have mercy." Mattie bent and picked up the paper and the pen at the same time. She unfolded the paper and read it aloud.

"Wait for word at the Postmaster's... that says Postmaster's, doesn't it, Franklin?" She tipped the paper toward her brother and pointed. He squinted at it.

"Can't say nothin' else. Must be the Postmaster's."

"Instructions will follow." She looked at Franklin. "I guess we can't do anything else tonight. I hope Lauren is okay."

"I'm sure she is," Franklin said confidently.

Dylan thought it was a good time to reveal himself. He wouldn't have stayed hidden if he hadn't thought his presence might draw attention. The two siblings seemed to be doing quite well getting away with what they were doing without being suspected by anyone at all.

He tilted his head and looked around the corner before marching out in the open.

"Here you both are," he said, not loudly but as casually as he could. "You must have gotten lost. Come on. I'll show you where to go."

The look of shock on Mattie's face was quickly replaced by one of amusement. She and Franklin followed Dylan as he went around the hat shop next door to the jailhouse and went through the alley on the other side of that building instead.

When he looked back, Mattie was right behind him, with Franklin not far behind her.

Their eyes locked for a moment. Dylan felt a rush of heat slide through him from his head to his toes. He wondered if she felt anything like that.

"We're just going to have to go back to the boarding house and rest for the night. At least you have a plan now."

"You heard all of that?"

"Most of it, I reckon. That was a real good idea, Mattie. Good thinking." He smiled at her, hoping the intensity of his feelings for her didn't show.

"Why, thank you, sir. I think a good night's sleep is a very good idea."

"Tomorrow, we'll go with you to the Postmaster's office. All of us will. And we'll figure out a plan from there."

"You don't think they'll be upset if they know we're working with you, do you?" Franklin asked.

"I don't see why they would," Dylan responded. "We aren't the law. We're just two fellas tryin' to help."

"I hope you're right," Franklin continued. "I don't

want anything to happen to Mattie. Not while I'm around."

"You are the best brother ever, you know that?" Mattie asked, giving her brother a brilliant smile.

Dylan liked seeing it. If he'd had any siblings, he would hope they would care about each other as much as Mattie and Franklin.

## 18

Mattie slept much better than she expected she would. When she woke up the next morning, she felt refreshed and invigorated, ready to go search for her sister and vanquish some evil outlaws.

She hopped out of bed and started a fire in the small hearth. When it was going strong, she filled a pail that was hanging from a hook beside the opening of the fireplace with water from the pitcher on her dresser. She placed it on the coals in the fire and quickly got dressed so she could visit the water closet down the hall.

By the time she was back in her room, the water in the fireplace had heated up. She used it to take a sponge bath before dressing in the same clothes she'd had on only moments ago and the entire day before. She would have to buy something clean from the local general store or the dress shop. She had money, but any bags she might have brought would have been left on the train, so neither she nor her brother brought any with them.

She planned to pick up one of those papers she'd seen the day before to see what the article was about. She hadn't read the headline. She was too focused on the picture and the fact that Dylan might see it.

After she was dressed, she went to the door that led to the room one over—Franklin's room. She knocked on it and tried the knob, but it was locked.

"Franklin, open the door," she called through. When her knock was met with silence, she wondered if he was even in there. Perhaps he was in the water closet, too. Or had already gone out to get breakfast and coffee.

She tried the doorknob again, but it wasn't stuck. It was locked.

She left her room behind after straightening her bedclothes. She didn't like to leave it looking a mess, and she was a restless sleeper, twisting and turning until her blankets were all over the bed.

Mattie glanced at the door on the other side of

her room where Dylan was, wondering if either of the businessmen were awake.

It didn't matter to her. She was more interested in seeing her brother than she was Dylan or Luke, which might have come as a surprise to anyone else. She went to the door of her brother's room and knocked. Still, there was no answer. She turned the knob and pushed the door open. He must have gone out. If he was still in there, this door would have been locked, while the one in between their rooms would have been unlocked.

He wasn't in the room. She looked around, though there was nowhere he could or would hide. There was a note on the bed, though, and she hurried to it. He must have gone for breakfast. That was the kind of considerate brother he was—

Mattie halted when she was a foot away from the bed, staring down at the note. The words were not written in her brother's handwriting. The letters were formed into blocks. Franklin had no need to write like that. He knew cursive. His handwriting was legible. This looked like it had been written by a child.

She leaped toward the bed and snatched the note up, staring at it, holding it between her two shaking hands.

"No," she breathed. "No, no, no, no."

With tears in her eyes, she ran from the room, bolting down the hall toward Dylan's door and banging on it violently when she got there.

"Dylan," she shrieked, tears ripping through her throat as the word came out. "Dylan. Dylan!"

She heard stomping as Dylan crossed the room to his door. When he yanked it open, he was standing before her with his shirt unbuttoned and untucked, his jeans on, and his hair a tousled mess of brown waves. His eyes were wide with concern.

"What's wrong, Mattie?" he demanded sharply.

Mattie handed him the note, her hand shaking like a leaf in the wind.

"They took him, Dylan, they took him." She wailed the words, her voice high and terrified. The next moment, Dylan came toward her until he was just inches from her. He placed one hand on her shoulder and leaned out to look both ways down the hallway. In the next moment, he was pulling her into the room, folding his arms around her and hugging her tightly.

If she hadn't been so thoroughly terrified for her brother, she would have enjoyed that very much. But as it was, all she could think about was Franklin. Where had they taken him? What were they doing to him? His arm was hurt. He was injured. If he got an infection, he could die. The thoughts raced through her mind, making her heart pound and her tears fall faster.

"Shhh," Dylan said, comfortingly. "We're gonna take care of this, Mattie. I don't want you to be afraid. Luke and I are going to help you find him. Get yourself together now, honey. He's fine."

"But... but..." She hiccupped but was determined to get her words out. "What if they... took him because... they don't have... Lauren anymore... I don't..."

He stopped her with a soothing hand on the back of her head and a kiss on the forehead. "Shh. Don't think like that. You know they're both alive and well. You know that, don't you?"

Mattie didn't know that. She wanted to know that. But she didn't know it.

"I don't... I don't..."

"You do," Dylan insisted, bending over to look her directly in the eyes. He cupped her face in his large, smooth hands and looked directly into her eyes. "You *do* know it, Mattie." His voice was so confident. She could feel herself calming as she held his gaze. "You *do* know it. There is *no way* Franklin is dead. I barely know him, and I feel like somehow I would know. So I know *you have* to know. Now gather your courage and come with me. We're going to fix this situation."

Mattie pulled in a deep breath and watched as Dylan finished getting dressed. He hurried to the door between his room and Luke's, buttoning his shirt and tucking it into his unbelted pants. He took a moment from the task to knock on the door, which was immediately pulled open as if Luke was on the other side.

She could see Luke was completely dressed, boots and all. He even had his hat in his hand. As soon as he pulled the door open, he passed Dylan and came directly over to her.

She stared up at him, seeing he was as serious and concerned as Dylan.

"You heard all of it, didn't you?" she asked, her voice shaking.

He nodded. He didn't say anything for a few seconds and then leaned in to say, "Dylan's right. This has gone on long enough. Let's go get them."

Mattie had no earthly idea how these men planned to find her brother and sister and rescue them. But she thanked God they had sat down in her train car. She wasn't sure she could have done anything useful all on her own by herself. She would have been a slave to the kidnappers until they decided to ask their father for ransom before shooting them all dead.

The thought made her shudder. She hurried out after Dylan and Luke, determined to be a participant and not a hindrance to the rescue efforts.

## 19

When Luke turned to him and asked for the note, Dylan handed it to him and started to pull on his boots. He had only scanned through it, thinking more about comforting Mattie than reading what it said.

"Read it out loud, Luke," he said. "It will help us figure out what to do."

"We have the brother. Now you have to help us with the big heist. Don't screw up again. You will break our boys out and help us rob the bank. Then we will let your sister and brother go. Don't fail us again. Their lives are in your hands." Luke's voice had turned hard and angry by the end of the letter. He swiped it roughly through the air, letting out a frustrated growl. "What complete rubbish. Why are they trying to involve you in all of this?"

Mattie's face darkened.

Dylan watched her after he finished with his boots and standing up.

"You might as well know I know who you are," he said, hoping his announcement wouldn't hurt or frighten her. "I saw the paper yesterday while I was out. I saw that you are the daughter of Judge Holbrook in Bighorn."

"Carter Holbrook?" Luke asked, shock in his voice. He swiveled his eyes to Mattie and scanned her. "Okay, yeah, I see the resemblance. I know both your parents."

Mattie blinked at him, looking stunned.

Luke grinned. "Don't look so shocked. Practically everyone knows your parents, at least your father. You are from good stock."

Dylan laughed at the strange compliment that made Mattie sound like cattle. She had an amused look on her face, too, which relieved Dylan.

"So now that we've got that out in the open, is there anything else you can tell us about this so we won't be surprised by anything?"

Mattie looked thoughtful, her hazel eyes lifting

to the ceiling as if the answers were written there. After a few moments, she looked back at him, shaking her head. "Really nothing I can think of right now, Dylan. But I'll tell you anything I think of if and when it comes to my mind."

"Okay. That will work. First of all, we can't break those bandits out of jail. That's not..." He shook his head, bewilderment making him speechless. "That's just not something we can do."

"I agree," Mattie stated, nodding. "We don't have criminal minds. I don't even want to think like a criminal."

"That means," Dylan went on, "that we'll have to find out where those two are being held. They can't be far. They wouldn't leave the area by much knowing their buddies are in the cells, and this is the bank they want to rob." He said the last part of the last sentence with heavy sarcasm in his voice. "Foolish idiots. I'm not a criminal, and I could do better than this."

Mattie's intense eyes turned to him. "They've got both my siblings, Dylan. I think they're doing a pretty good job."

Dylan sucked in a breath and felt his cheeks flushing hotly. "You're right. I'm sorry."

"I swear to God if they hurt even a hair on those kids' heads, their heads are gonna roll," Luke growled under his breath. Dylan was slightly amused to hear the ferocity with which his friend spoke about a man he barely knew and a woman he didn't know at all. "I've got an idea. Let's go to Franklin's room and see if we can figure anything out. Maybe we'll find a clue that could tell us where to look next."

Mattie was already on her feet and heading for the door. The men came close behind her.

"Franklin had his door locked when he went to bed last night," Mattie said over her shoulder as they went down the hall. "But it was open when I got here earlier to fetch him."

At the door to Franklin's room, Mattie paused. Neither Dylan nor Luke pushed her to continue. She would do so in her own time.

It didn't take long for Mattie to get herself together. Dylan was proud of her when she squared her shoulders and reopened the door.

The three entered the room, and Dylan examined it closely. The bed was a wreck. Franklin must be a restless sleeper. There was no blood anywhere to be seen, which was a very good thing. There didn't seem to be signs of a scuffle, and the door to the room had not been jimmied.

"Why would Franklin have opened the door to the kidnappers?" Dylan mumbled under his breath.

"He wouldn't have," Mattie replied without looking at him. She was slowly straightening the bedcovers, her face dark and dreary.

"There are scuff marks on this windowsill," Luke said, "but no sign whether it was Franklin and the kidnapper who put them there. Besides, why go out the windowsill when the door is so much easier?"

Dylan let out a heavy sigh, licking and chewing his lips, his eyes roaming around the room.

"There's only one explanation for how someone could have come in this room without Franklin opening the door," he said, moving his eyes between Mattie and Luke. They both gave him their full attention, obviously waiting for him to continue. "Actually two ways, if you count Franklin actually opening the door to them, which I can't see happening. Someone had to have had a key."

"Only the manager has a key other than us, right?" Luke said, sounding confused. "I can't see that man being involved with these thieves."

"Unless they took one of his relatives, too," Mattie remarked mournfully.

Luke grunted. "Two kidnappings in one night? They kidnapped a member of the manager's family so they could get a key to come and kidnap your family member? It just doesn't make sense. I don't think much of these outlaws, but they can't possibly be that stupid."

"You know what?" Dylan said suddenly, a thought coming to his mind. "I think I saw a board down there—a peg board with keys on it. Each one had two keys on it except for the rooms that are rented out."

"And they only have one," Luke murmured.

Dylan nodded, moving his eyes between the two of them. "That's right. It's behind the counter, though. Let's go see what the boarding manager has to say for himself, shall we?"

The three of them left Franklin's room in a hurry. Dylan could tell Mattie did not want to be in there at all. He felt for her, though he couldn't imagine what she was really going through. He had no siblings of his own. He didn't know what it felt like to love one, miss one, or be worried about one.

But he'd seen the love between the brother and sister consistently for the last twenty-four hours or so. And he had no doubt that she was terrified she wouldn't see Franklin or Lauren alive again.

He kept himself from reaching out to comfort her. He was afraid it would be too much. He had already taken her in his arms that morning without even thinking about it. It had felt good, too. He wanted to do that again—a bunch of times.

The boarding house manager's name was Clinton Bixby. He was seated in a large, tall chair on the other side of the chest-high counter where people signed in. He was on his feet as soon as he spotted them coming from the hallway to the rooms.

Mattie was nervous. She didn't like to confront people who were smiling at her. If the argument was already ongoing, she didn't mind telling someone what she thought. But when they were already smiling and were unaware they were about to be scolded harshly, she had a hard time doing it at all.

"Someone was in Franklin's room last night," Dylan said. Mattie was eternally grateful he'd decided to take the lead. As much as she wanted to be in charge and ready to fight, she was being weakened by the bandits stealing away her brother. She felt like she'd been battered by a large bat. Her heart slammed in her chest every time she thought they might hurt Franklin even more than he was already injured. What if they truly broke his arm by mishandling him?

Mattie's heart quaked.

It was bad enough that her sister was gone. She could barely survive without Franklin. He was her constant companion. He was smart and capable and would be a successful doctor one day. Nothing could happen to him.

What would she tell her parents if something happened to him? Tears came to her eyes, but she hid them from Dylan and Luke. She couldn't tell Dylan how guilty she felt. She was the oldest. She was supposed to keep both her younger siblings safe. But not only had she lost her sister to bandits, she'd let her brother come along and get taken as well. It was all her fault.

"Hey." Dylan got her attention, waving one hand in front of her eyes to bring her out of the daze she'd put herself in. "You there? You with us?"

Mattie blinked several times rapidly and focused on him through her tear-filled eyes.

"Stop it, Mattie," Dylan reprimanded her gently. "I can see you're thinking bad thoughts. No bad thoughts."

"I... I don't know anything about that," Clint was saying, his wide eyes moving between the two men, who were both taller and younger than he. Luke looked ready to kill, which probably didn't make the manager any more at ease. Mattie didn't care, though. She wanted the man to be uncomfortable. Her brother had been taken, and as far as she was concerned, he'd helped them do it.

"I need to find him," she said weakly, her eyes on the short, plump man across the counter from her. "You *must* know something. You couldn't have been sleeping soundly when someone was in here stealing a key from your peg board."

The manager's face went white, and his eyes flicked to the peg board.

"As I told your friends, Miss," he replied, his voice as weak and afraid as hers, "I did notice the key was gone this morning but assumed one of you had taken it to use. I didn't realize he was your brother. I am sorry."

"You sure you didn't know?"

Dylan asked. Mattie looked at his face, wondering what he was thinking. Suddenly, she realized he could easily have seen the photograph in the newspaper. Their names had been under the picture. What if he had offered his assistance to the bandits?

Mattie mentally dismissed the idea. There was just too much coincidence involved. And by the look of utter terror and despair on the manager's face, she believed he had nothing whatsoever to do with the kidnapping.

Distraught, she turned away from all three men.

"No. I do not know what happened to the young man. I am so very..." He stopped talking.

Mattie waited for him to continue, and when he didn't right away, she turned back to see Luke and Dylan had gotten closer to the manager and were staring him down. The manager's eyes flicked from one to the other and back again, shrinking away from them. He didn't speak again until suddenly, his eyes lit up.

Mattie could see he'd thought of something. She pushed between the two tall men and joined them in peering directly at the manager.

"What is it?" she asked urgently. "What did you remember? I saw you remember something. What is it?"

Clint blinked, his eyes moving back and forth as

he nodded vigorously. "Yes. Yes. I did see something. I do remember something. But I had no idea it was anything like this."

"Well, what did you see?" Dylan asked impatiently.

Clint's eyes widened. "It was... it was the early hours. Maybe four? I got up to use the closet and get some water to drink. I looked at the clock in the hall as I passed. I was in the kitchen a short time later and heard something outside. I looked out, and there were two men with lanterns going down the street. They had someone between them. I remember because they looked so awkward holding him. I thought he was a drunk."

"Why did they look awkward?" Dylan asked the question on Mattie's mind, sounding confused.

"Because the man in the middle had one arm around one man's shoulders but not the other. So the other man was trying to carry him by the waist. Does that make sense?"

Mattie's heart fell into her stomach. At least they hadn't tried to break Franklin's arm for good. She turned her eyes to Dylan, who locked his with hers.

"Because Franklin's arm is in the sling. He must have been sleeping with it. They wouldn't have known about it otherwise."

"Shows a bit more compassion than I'm used to for criminals," Luke responded.

"You know a lot of criminals?" Mattie asked, not meaning to sound suspicious.

"No, no," Luke denied the accusation, shaking his head.

Mattie could tell when Dylan spoke, he wanted to get away from that subject. "Which direction did you see them going?" he asked the manager urgently.

"I think I saw them..." Clint hesitated. He waved one hand, moving out from behind the counter. The three followed him to the kitchen and to the window through which he'd seen the men. He pointed.

"That way. They were going that way."

Mattie was disheartened. The man had pointed in the direction of the town. Then again, if he'd pointed out of town, that wouldn't have been any better.

She was surprised when Dylan grabbed her hand and pulled on her. "Let's go. Come on, Luke. Let's go out there and see what we can see."

The three hurried to the door, and Dylan opened it, holding it they passed in front of him. As soon as they were outside, Dylan stopped them saying quietly, "We need to go slow and sure. Together.

Don't go off on your own. Stay by the walls but try not to look suspicious. Keep your eye out for anything strange."

"We can't stay against the walls," Mattie replied in a low voice. "They were dragging him down the middle of the street. I want to see if there are any drag marks left. It's still early yet. Maybe they haven't been trampled or wiped away by passing horses and people and wagon wheels."

Feeling a strong sense of eager nervousness, Mattie pulled her hand from Dylan's grasp and hurried out in the middle of the street.

"Mattie. Wait," Dylan called out to her, but it was more of a dramatic whisper than anything else. She glanced back at him but kept going. She wanted to hurry. He was right. She felt as exposed as ever. She felt like any moment now, a bullet would come whizzing through the air and puncture her stomach or her heart.

But then why would they kill her? They needed her. She was supposed to get the two criminals out of jail, wasn't she?

She peered down the street, looking on both sides for a sign. When she saw it, she turned back to the men and called out, "The Postmaster's. It's that way."

She was triumphant for two reasons. The men had dragged Franklin in that same direction, and if they were watching or listening, they would think she was going to check for a letter of instruction. That's where they'd told her to go. That's where she would go.

But not if she saw drag marks taking her down a side street. She'd make up an excuse. She'd find a way.

## 21

Dylan came up behind her, his eyes on the ground. He knew exactly what she was doing when she called back to them about the Postmaster's. He took a moment to wonder if the bandits had any idea that he and Luke had been the ones to drive the train to the Trumperton station. They needed Mattie, he realized that. But did they need him and Luke? Maybe one but not both? Were either of them in danger being in the middle of the street? He tried not to think about it too much as they searched the ground for drag marks.

"Hey, you two," Luke remarked casually, crooking his index finger at them. They got closer to him, continuing their slow progress down the street. Mattie was making a big show of taking in all her surroundings, including the sky and the ground below. He got on one side of Luke and Mattie the other.

"You see what I see?" he asked, keeping his voice low, flicking one finger almost invisibly toward the ground in front of him. He stopped and stretched but only for a second. He probably realized it wouldn't be very believable.

"I see them." Mattie's voice came out in a harsh whisper.

Dylan worried for a moment that she would start crying again, which would greatly hinder her ability to see any drag marks in the road at all.

"Follow me," Luke said, "Just go where I go. Don't look down anymore. Let me do that. So if they're watching..." He let his words trail off, knowing Dylan and Mattie understood.

Dylan was proud of his friend. He was also thanking God Luke was the one he'd been trapped in this adventure with. If he was going to have to fight outlaws with anyone, Luke was the man to pick.

Dylan let his eyes roam around him. He couldn't imagine there were more than five hundred people in that town at the very most. It was probably more like *one* hundred. There were very few people walking around, the saloon was quiet, and there was no one in the restaurant at all when they passed. He was left wondering if everyone on the train had already left.

They probably had, as much of them were complaining about the delay.

One side street and ten minutes later, Luke stopped. They'd left the residences and shops behind and were walking down a dirt road flanked by trees that became less and less sparse until they were all that could be seen.

Dylan looked down. The dirt road had turned to grass with two wheel marks driven into the ground to leave behind separate trails going on down the road. There were no more drag marks.

Dylan was ready to be disappointed and have to comfort Mattie when he looked ahead of them.

"I don't believe it," he murmured.

"I suggest we get out of sight right now," Luke said before lurching to one side to hide behind a tree.

"You think they took him to that house?" Mattie asked, hurrying to join him, her eyes wide and focused on the house the dirt road led them to.

"Yeah, I'll bet they are," Luke said. "I'm telling

you, I think less and less of the intelligence of these people the further we get into this."

Dylan had to agree with his friend. He could tell by the look on Mattie's face she did, too.

"I'm glad," she said quietly. "Makes it easier for us to stop them."

Dylan had his eyes on the house, watching for any movement through the windows. It was a very small cabin, painted a light green color with dark green trim and shutters. The door was dark brown and arched on top. Vines had grown up along the walls of the house. He was willing to bet no one had occupied the house for quite a while before the bandits got it.

"You think they're renting it legitimately?" Luke asked quietly.

"I wouldn't even know how to find out something like that," Dylan replied under his breath. "I'm going to go look around a little closer."

"No, don't," Mattie cried out softly. "You could get hurt."

Dylan was touched by her concern. He gave her a warm look, thinking someday he would like to show her how much that meant to him. "Your brother is already hurt. I'll be careful. We've got to get them out of there if that's where they are."

"They might shoot you," Mattie hissed, her eyes turning soft. It felt like someone had put a hand around his heart and started squeezing and releasing.

"I have to do this, Mattie. I'll be all right. You just stay here with Luke. Okay? Promise me? Promise you'll stay back here with Luke. Don't follow me."

"But they're my brother and sister. I should be the one going."

"So they can get all three of you? You can't help us get them out if you're in there, too. Now hush. Let me do this to make sure they are even in there. Then we'll talk about what to do next."

Mattie looked upset but said nothing more.

Luke gave him a confident look. "You can do this, Dylan. And I've got your back. I'll be watching. And I'll be ready." He pulled his gun from the holster at his side and held it up, cocking the hammer.

The sound did give Dylan more confidence. He nodded.

It felt strange to leave them behind as he went toward the house, staying low and hidden behind the trees. He wasn't sure whether what he was feeling was concern or what it was. He just knew that he had to do whatever he could to get Mattie's siblings back. He felt obligated for some reason.

Dylan approached the house with great caution. There were two windows in the front of the house, on either side of the arched door. Two windows appeared on the side, as well. He came up alongside the house and moved so he was crouching behind a bush, peering through the holes made by the tangled limbs and leaves. He leaned his head to the left and the right until he got a clear view of the side of the house.

He saw no movement inside at first. When a figure stood up from an apparent sitting position and moved away from the window, Dylan's heart nearly seized in his chest.

He stayed where he was, frozen, watching the front door to see if someone was coming out. Had they seen him? Was that even one of the bandits? How would he know? It could be anyone.

"No," he mumbled to himself. "If it was just anyone, the drag marks wouldn't have led us here."

No one came through the front door. The person he'd seen stand up came back into his view and sat down. It was a man. That was all Dylan knew. Whether he was a bandit would remain to be seen.

As he looked at the house more closely, he noticed something at the back of the house that looked strange.

He squinted his eyes and stared. Was that a step? A step leading down? Like into a cellar?

That was something to explore.

## 22

Dylan stayed low as he moved across the back lawn. His heart slammed in his chest. He could only pray he wouldn't be seen. He really didn't want to get shot.

He got down almost to his belly and crawled toward the back of the house. The closer he got, the more he could see the distinct markings of rock steps, grass growing out from the edges and nearly covering the steps.

Dylan looked up at the window above his head. It was covered with a drape on the inside and prevented anyone from seeing in or out of the glass. That was a good thing for him, he thought, as he lowered himself down the steps, feet first. He held onto the steps, eager to get to the window he'd spotted. It was also grimy and had vines growing around it, practically invading the walls themselves.

He could barely see anything when he looked through the dirty glass. He had to focus. There was light coming from somewhere, probably a different window, as this one was covered by foliage.

That light was enough to give him a view of what was inside the nearly empty cellar.

What he did see sent chills all over his body.

He saw Franklin sitting in a chair, a bag over his head. Dylan recognized the young man's clothes, which he must have slept in since he didn't have anything else with him. Dylan's heart hurt to see what they had done to the young man, though he supposed he should have been grateful they hadn't taken advantage of his injury to hurt him more. Instead of tying his hands behind his back, they had Franklin cross his good arm over his chest, and they looped the rope around his entire upper body, securing him to the chair.

Dylan moved his eyes to the other chair where the young woman was. He could see she was wearing a party dress and pretty shoes. He could even see the long rip in her nylons. She also had a bag over her head, but she was tied with her hands behind the chair. Both of them had their ankles tied to the legs of the chairs they sat in.

When light burst through the room from the door at the top of the stairs being opened, Dylan's heart leaped into his throat. He moved back quicky, hoping he wasn't seen. He heard men's boots stomping down the steps, followed by a deep voice. He strained his ears but couldn't understand what was being said.

He waited until the boots went back upstairs before going further down the steps to probe the doorway. It was sealed shut from years of not being used. The growth around it made it almost impossible to even see. He examined it carefully. The window was too small to go through, even for Mattie.

They weren't getting in that way. It would take way too much noise trying to unseal the doorway. They'd need pickaxes and shovels. If it was permanently sealed on the other side, they would be completely out of luck after putting in a lot of effort.

Dylan hurried back up the steps and carefully made his way back to Luke and Mattie, who were waiting for him with eager faces.

"Well?" Mattie asked. "Did you see them?"

"They are there," he stated bluntly. "I saw them."

The look on Mattie's face was priceless. He could tell she didn't know whether to be relieved and happy or just plain frightened.

"We have to go get them," she cried out, surging toward the house. Both men stepped directly in her way, blocking her.

"No, no," they both said at exactly the same time.

"You can't go barging in there," Dylan exclaimed. "Have you lost your mind? We have to come up with a plan. Now listen to me. They are in the cellar. The door to that cellar is completely sealed off and blocked by overgrowth. There is a window, but it's much too small for anyone to crawl through. Including you." He said the last part quickly when she opened her mouth to volunteer. At least, that's what he assumed she was going to say. When she closed her mouth, he knew he'd been right.

"So, what do you think we should do?" Luke asked.

Dylan ran his fingers over his short stubbly beard. "We're going to have to wait until they leave. They're bound to leave eventually, if anything, to take that letter to the Postmaster or to get something to eat or *something*."

"Maybe we should just go to the sheriff and get a couple of deputies to—"

"No," Mattie barked, sounding like a small dog. Dylan and Luke looked at her. "I don't want to get in trouble for helping these men. We need to get my brother and sister out ourselves. Then we can get the sheriff involved, and we can get out of here. It will be a lot easier to explain after we get them out."

"They aren't going to do put you in a cell, Mattie," Dylan said. "We need to have more help. They will understand, I'm sure they will."

Mattie's face settled into a frown that Dylan didn't understand. He was taken aback when she lashed out at him, saying, "You just don't care if I get put in jail. You already don't think women are worth enough to vote or hold a high position in a business."

Dylan was speechless but wanted desperately to say something. He had no idea where this was coming from.

"I didn't say anything like that, Mattie. Please. Hear me out. You can't do anything on your own, and both of us think we should—"

"I know what you think," Mattie cried out, her voice trembling. "I know you don't think I can do anything on my own. But if you want to go to the sheriff, you'll do it without me. I'll get my brother and sister out all by myself without your help."

"Wait, what are you talking about?" Dylan was stunned when Mattie turned around and ran off.

"Where is she going?" Luke asked, concern for the troubled woman loud in his voice.

"I don't know. I can't even yell at her to come back. Those men in there will hear me."

"Well, come on. I reckon we can't just let her run off on her own."

Dylan didn't get any relief from his confusion as he and Luke took off after the woman. She was running through the trees haphazardly, apparently trying to lose them. He had no idea why she was doing what she was doing or where she planned to go. Could the thought of them going to the sheriff really have sent her into such a tailspin?

"She has every reason to be afraid," Luke said as they hurried along after the woman. "But she has to know there's nothing she can do on her own."

"I think her guilt is overwhelming her," Dylan mentioned, her distraught face hovering in his mind's eye. "I know she thinks she's responsible for a lot of what's happened. I didn't tell her about the engineer getting killed because of that."

"Well, we can't let her go off half-cocked. She needs our help. Our protection. Whether she likes it or not." Luke glanced at his friend. "Your previous admonitions probably didn't help."

"Maybe not, but that's done now. I'm looking at things a different way now."

Luke gave his friend a longer look. "Oh? Is that so?"

"Yeah. I'm... I'm gonna change the theme of the magazine we're gonna put out."

Luke chuckled. "What are we gonna change it to?"

Dylan's sarcastic look made Luke laugh out loud. "I don't know," Dylan retorted. "But I'll be sure to let you know."

## 23

"What a frustrating woman," Dylan murmured as he and Luke left the small house behind where the siblings were being kept.

"Where do you think she went?"

"She has nowhere she can go," Dylan replied to his friend's query. "She doesn't know anyone here, at least, I don't think she does. She never mentioned she did to me."

Luke was shaking his head in agreement with Dylan. "No, I'm pretty sure she doesn't know anyone either. It seems like something she might have mentioned. Or her brother would have, and he gave me the impression all of this came out of the blue."

"She had to have gone to the boarding house. If

there's one thing I know for certain, it's that she is not a stupid woman. She'd have nowhere else she can go."

They were at the end of the path leading up to the house and turned toward town. Another five-minute walk and they would be back at the boarding house.

The two men said nothing else as they got to town and the boarding house. Dylan went in first with Luke right behind him. Neither acknowledged Clint. They just passed him by. It may not have been his fault, but he could have done something, and he didn't.

Dylan reached Mattie's door first. He knocked and leaned closer, one ear toward the door.

"Mattie?" he called out, trying the knob. It was locked. He rattled it several times. "Mattie, if you're in there, please open up. We need to talk to you. No one is going to the sheriff. I don't want you to be afraid, and if you're afraid, then we won't do it. Okay? Please open the door. Mattie? Plea..."

He stopped when the door was pulled open—slowly at first and then all the way as she stepped back into her room. She turned and left the door open for them to come in, going to the window. She stood there, a melancholy look on her face, her arms folded in front of her chest.

Dylan went straight to her. It hurt his heart to see her looking this way. He wished he could just snap his fingers and make it all go away. Then again, if it hadn't been for this predicament, he would likely never have met her.

That would have been a tragedy all in itself.

He stopped right behind her, trying to quickly decide whether he should touch her or not.

Finally, when he couldn't resist it any longer, he stepped up behind her and grasped her upper arms. He squeezed but only gently, lowering his head, so his lips were near her ear.

"Don't be afraid," he whispered. He saw her close her eyes and pull in a deep breath. "I saw them. They look fine."

Mattie's eyes snapped open, and she gave him a sharp look.

"Not fine," he responded quickly. "They aren't fine. They look fine. Considering the circumstances. We're going to get them out, all right? I know it. I guarantee it. We will rescue them."

Mattie's anger dissipated as quickly as it had shown up. Her shoulders slumped, and she tilted her head so it was resting on his chest. "It's all my fault," she moaned, once more closing her eyes.

"You stop saying that right now, little Mattie," Dylan responded with obvious affection. He couldn't help it. It was the way he felt. He was hit by Cupid's arrow, and there was no going back now. Once again, he leaned his head down close to hers, pulling her back toward him by her upper arms in a very gentle way. "The only fault here lies with those thieves. You've done nothing wrong. Nothing."

"How can you say that?" Mattie asked, the pain in her voice ebbing through her words.

"I'm going to the Postmaster's," Luke said abruptly, turning on his heel and disappearing through the door. He had to duck slightly to get out and pulled the door closed behind him.

Once he was gone, the heat between Mattie and Dylan only seemed to increase. Dylan's heart slammed in his chest. He could feel her body, so close to his, so tense and rigid. She was terrified for her siblings, something he couldn't relate to but could still empathize about.

"You've been one of the bravest women I've ever seen," he murmured into her ear, noticing when she sucked in a sharp breath and closed her eyes. "I've always taken for granted that women are nurturers, servants to those around them simply because they want to be. It's in their instincts. I believe it's in your instinct to fight, to be brave, to never let go or flee from peril. I'm so impressed with everything you've been doing. Everything. I hate that you feel so guilty. I wish I could take it from you."

"Ah, but you can't," Mattie responded just as softly, leaving her eyes closed. "I wasn't... I can't say I've been the best sister for Lauren if I'm very honest with you."

Dylan pulled his eyebrows together in confusion, not believing that could be possible.

"That's ridiculous," he said softly. "I'll bet you didn't hesitate to drop everything to come and rescue her. That's sisterly love."

"No, that's being afraid of my parents. They will kill me when they find out what she's done. I am to blame, don't you see? Their failure is also my failure. I've failed them. I've failed Ma and Pa. Maybe you should get away from me before I fail you, too. Maybe you or Luke will end up dead because of me." She pulled out of his hands, turning away, closer to the window. He heard it as she broke into new sobs, trying to keep them as quiet as possible.

Dylan couldn't help himself. He gathered her in his arms the way he had done before and held on, swaying back and forth gently. "There, there," he said softly. "You aren't in the state of mind to be thinking about things like that. My mother once said not to hesitate on taking my time to get a job done. She said hurrying makes waste and destruction happen. Disastrous results, she said, every single time."

"Your mother is a wise woman." To Dylan, it sounded like Mattie was just trying to be polite. He gave her a sad smile.

"Thank you."

The door opened, and Luke came through swiftly. He slammed it shut behind him and hurried to them.

"So here's the letter. He says he wants to do this at one in the morning. But tomorrow. He says they need supplies."

"Tomorrow night?"

Dylan and Mattie slowly separated. He didn't want to take his hands from her, but he knew he had to. They moved apart, and each took seats, Mattie in a chair by the window, Dylan on the edge of the bed. He held out his hand, and Luke handed the letter to him.

He scanned the words written there and nodded. "Yep. Makes sense."

"We aren't going to really break him out, are we?" Mattie sounded afraid. Dylan took one of her hands and squeezed it with a smile.

"No, of course not. We'll be ready." Luke moved closer to the fire. "In the meantime, let's get kindling and wood for the fireplace. It's going to get cold tonight. I can feel it."

"I need to eat," Mattie stated bluntly.

The men gave her curious looks. She shrugged.

"We have to eat, don't we? Franklin would tell us to eat."

"All right." Luke nodded. "Let's go see what's for dinner down in the dining room. I smell something cooking right now, and it's making my stomach growl. You want to?"

"Yes," Mattie responded.

"With pleasure," Dylan replied, nodding.

## 24

The evening meal offered by the boarding house to its guests was beef stew with more veggies than meat. When she'd been eating it, Mattie had wondered where all the meat was. She'd concluded that the boarding house hadn't had enough meat to really make the stew, so they'd added way more vegetables than necessary to make up for the lack of it.

Still, it was a delicious concoction, and she'd eaten nearly two bowls herself. She'd noticed Dylan had two bowls, as well, and then finished off the rest of hers.

Back in Dylan's room, they sat around chatting for hours until Luke finally fell asleep, in what looked to Mattie like a terribly uncomfortable position. He was seated in one of the cushioned chairs, his long legs stretched out in front of him, his head laid on the back of the chair, so his face was toward the ceiling. It was as though once he laid his head back and closed his eyes, he was asleep.

Mattie listened to the light snoring sound he made as he slept.

"Have you known Luke for a long time?" she asked Dylan.

The two were both seated on the couch, one at the end, the other at the opposite end. Both were facing each other by sitting at an angle, and Mattie's leg, though pulled up on the couch, was covered by her dress. He was in the same position, his leg in front of him between them. One of his arms rested on top of the back of the couch.

"He's been my best friend forever," Dylan responded, grinning. "He's like a brother to me."

"Do you have any siblings?"

Dylan looked regretful for a moment. She noticed, though, that the emotion seemed fleeting, and when Dylan spoke, she thought she understood why.

"No, I'm an only child. Luke is, too. Thankfully, we grew up so near each other we had only each other to play with. So we ended up becoming fast friends, good friends. We've watched out for each other all our lives."

"I'm sure you always will. How lovely. What a good thing to have. A friendship like yours."

"It has come in handy many times," Dylan responded, nodding, his eyes moving to Luke, who snorted and rubbed one finger under his nose in his sleep. He turned his head to the side and remained asleep. "He's been my laughter and my support and my encouragement and sometimes even my courage over the years. I hope to have been the same for him."

"I'm sure you were."

Dylan gave her a warm look of affection that made her wish he was sitting closer. How nice it would have been to take his hand, just to hold, while they talked. Just touching him would be enough for her. To have skin-on-skin contact. She already knew his hands were smooth and soft, almost like a woman's. He had never swung a hammer, she was sure of that at least.

"It's a lot like a sibling situation," he continued, eyeing her closely. She didn't mind it. He could eye her all she wanted, closely or otherwise. "You and your brother are obviously very close. You can tell each other practically anything. There are no secrets between you, none that could be harmful anyway. Everyone has at least one or two things they keep to themselves. Being an open book to other people should be selective."

"I think so, too." Mattie looked into the crackling fire, thinking for a moment before swiveling her eyes back to him. "I'm sure there are plenty of things you don't go around telling everyone about that you will talk to Luke about."

"Can I ask how you got roped into this situation in the first place?" Dylan asked, reaching to the coffee table to his right and picking up his glass of wine. "You don't seem like the reckless type. I'm still reeling from the fact that these bandits didn't simply ask for ransom money from your father. You've grown up with a silver spoon in your mouth, haven't you?"

Mattie tried not to feel resentful of the phrase. She'd heard it before, and though it was true, it was still somewhat hurtful to her. It implied she was spoiled, which she definitely wasn't.

"I was born into a wealthy family, yes. That's my lot in life. And it's a much, much better lot than most have, I know. I try not to take advantage of that. I try to give back. I always have. But it's not just me. It's not even just Franklin and me. That might have made a difference. It's Lauren that has been a problem for a while."

Luke interrupted her with an abrupt loud snort. He didn't manage to wake himself up, though, and just turned his head to the side, quieting down again. He'd drawn the attention of both Mattie and Dylan for a moment.

Mattie looked back at Dylan. When she spoke, she had the tiniest of smiles and said, "Now that I've been so rudely interrupted, I will continue."

They both laughed softly.

"She lost her mind when she was about twelve." Mattie shook her head. "I don't know why. I understand she was upset when Papa died."

"Surely you don't think she is a part of all this. In league with the bandits, so to speak."

Dylan sounded as though he himself would be heartbroken to learn Lauren leaned toward the wrong side of the law.

Mattie narrowed her eyes at him. "When you saw her in the cellar, did she look like she was a part of it? In league with them, as you say?"

Dylan's face turned bright red. Mattie almost felt sorry for him, but his question had gotten under her skin.

"No," he stated plainly. "As a matter of fact, she

didn't. She was as much a prisoner as Franklin. I'm sorry for even suggesting such a thing."

Mattie shook her head, pulling the corners of her mouth down and pinching her lips together. "It's okay. The problem is that just because she's a prisoner now doesn't mean she didn't fall in with these men and encourage their bad behavior. She is troubled sometimes, she doesn't see how good things are for her and always wants more."

Mattie felt bad for talking about her sister in a negative way, but she was only telling the truth. Lauren had been a handful all her life, and now it was coming to a head.

"I'm sure you and your family have done all you could to keep her on the straight and narrow," Dylan stated gently.

She gazed at him, wishing the situation was more compatible with romance. She could definitely see herself falling in love with the man. He wasn't just good-looking. He was brave. He was fighting alongside her to rescue two people—one he barely knew, the other he didn't know at all.

"Thank you," she said softly. "Not just for saying that but for helping me with all this. Helping us."

Dylan shook his head. "I'm sure you and Franklin could have done just fine on your own. I don't think much would have changed if Luke and I weren't there."

Mattie pulled her eyebrows together. "No, Dylan. You and Luke have been a blessing to me right now. I would be by myself at this very moment, trying to deal with my brother being taken, along with my sister. It wouldn't surprise me if I had been captured along with Franklin if you two weren't here."

Dylan looked thoughtful. "I don't know about that."

"You don't?" She was curious.

"No," Dylan said, turning his eyes to meet with hers. He held her gaze as he spoke. "They wouldn't have anyone to get their men out of jail then, would they? And how do they expect us to help them?" He raised his hands and made air quotes around the word help.

"Well, we aren't going to anyway. We're going to get them out when it's convenient for us. Right?"

He grinned at her. "Right."

## 25

"Will you go over the plan with me one more time?" Mattie asked.

Dylan scanned her face, thinking how amazing it was that she had changed his entire way of thinking in less than two days. Her quick mind, her sharp wit, her high intelligence, and great common sense. Was there anything this woman couldn't do?

He was highly impressed and wanted to tell her so. But he didn't. It wasn't the right time. There were more important things to discuss.

He sat forward, clasping his hands together, his elbows on his knees. "So they want us to go hide after dark somewhere around the cells tomorrow night, right? They plan to meet us there." Dylan grinned, thinking how inept the thieves were. Nothing about their plan had made sense to him so far. He was beginning to wonder if this was the first job the "gang" had ever done. He had thoughts about Lauren, too.

It wasn't too far of a stretch, he felt, to think that perhaps Lauren, with her ill judgment, concocted the plan herself. Perhaps as a prank on her parents or a bid for freedom, even. And the plan had gone wrong somehow. He would bet his bottom dollar it started with Lauren and snowballed into a dangerous, chaotic mess, one in which Lauren got herself into just as much danger as she brought to her family.

Dylan scanned her face. How would she feel if she knew the engineer had died as a result of the train robbery?

He wouldn't be the one to tell her, that was certain.

"But we're not going to wait till then. Since we know where they are keeping your sister and brother, we'll just go there tomorrow and wait for them to leave. When they go, we'll go in and get them. Once you and they are safe on the way back to Bighorn, we'll get the sheriff to arrest the two that aren't in jail, and he can string them all up."

Mattie nodded, blinking, her face somewhat blank. He wondered what she was thinking. He thought it was an excellent plan. They knew more than the bandits thought they did. That was the only reason they'd been given extra time.

"Are you having doubts about the plan?" Dylan asked in a soft voice. "You look worried."

"I am worried," she admitted, slowly lifting her eyes to take in his face. "I'm worried that they will think we were involved. I told you before, what if Lauren knew these men? What if she had a part in this at the beginning? Will they put her in prison?"

Dylan shook his head. "For kidnapping herself? I don't see how they can do that."

"I don't know how *any* of it works," Mattie replied, her nervousness obvious in her voice. "And I'm terrified I'm going to end up in prison. I can't handle that, Dylan. I'll have to run away. I'll live a life on the run as a fugitive. Then I really will become an outlaw, won't I? A fugitive, running from the law. What if I take up a life of crime? Is that what God has in store for me?"

Dylan would have laughed, would have believed one hundred percent that Mattie was joking around, but the look on her face was deadly serious.

"You aren't going to prison, Mattie. Why are you even thinking like this?"

To his complete surprise, Mattie sat forward abruptly, buried her face in her hands, and began to sob quietly. Dylan scooted across the couch so that he was close to her. He put one arm around her shoulders and pulled her to him, so her head was resting on his chest. He kissed the top of her head, enjoying the softness of her hair against his lips. "What's gotten into you, Mattie? Why are you so upset? Please talk to me. Please tell me."

It took a moment for Mattie to respond. She had to stop crying, then hiccup and sniff a couple of times before she could lift her head and look into his eyes. "What if they charge me... with murder because... of the train... the driver of the... train..." Her shoulders jerked violently, and she began to sob, dropping her face again.

He pulled her into a warm hug, his heart racing. There was a strange feeling inhabiting his chest, a feeling of great sorry and trepidation. It was because of her. He couldn't bear to see her so fearful. So she'd found out about the engineer after all. He wondered just how much she knew about what happened after her brother pulled that cord. Had she watched him and Luke skirting the outside of the train, heading for the engine car?

Could they have helped in any way, or did they just run away from the scene?

Dylan wasn't going to let himself think the worst. He had to believe if Mattie and Franklin had seen them trying to escape, they would have offered to help. Not that they could have contributed much, but Dylan's father had always told him there was safety in numbers. You don't fight your biggest battle alone, he'd said. Always make sure you have a trusted friend to help you out.

That friend was Luke. And during his schoolboy days, a few others as well. In fact, they might have been called a gang, except they weren't.

"You didn't kill that man, Mattie," he whispered. "There was absolutely nothing you could have done to prevent what happened."

"I shouldn't have let Franklin pull the cord," she continued in a heartbroken tone. "I should have found another way. Just like we're doing something different tomorrow, not waiting to be told what to do and breaking two criminals out of jail. We're going to rescue Franklin and Lauren. That's what people with brains do."

Dylan sighed, nodding his head. "These outlaws

are the most dim-witted bunch I've ever seen. We don't have to worry about them outsmarting us, that's certain."

Mattie was surprised to hear a laugh escape from her lips. Lately, it had felt like she would never laugh again, not with any genuine sincerity. All they had to do was rescue her siblings. Then she would get her to laugh back.

"You should really be getting some sleep, Mattie," Dylan murmured, seeing the drawn lines in her face where she'd obviously been missing sleep. "You won't function tomorrow during our rescue mission if you don't get some good sleep."

"Yes, yes," Mattie grumbled in a way that tugged on Dylan's heartstrings. She dramatically pulled herself from the couch. She took a few steps away from him toward the door and stopped. He watched from behind her.

After a few moments of him admiring her backside, she turned and looked at him. He immediately lifted his eyes and smiled like the cat that had swallowed the canary.

"I, uh, I don't want to be alone tonight. Would it be all right if I slept on your floor tonight?"

Dylan was astonished that she'd even entertain

the idea of sleeping on his floor. When he answered, he enjoyed the look of utter surprise on her face.

"What? No. Absolutely not. You'll sleep in the bed. I will take the couch in here. No sense in you getting all bumped and bruised from the floor." He pushed himself from the couch, excited for a chance to be that close to Mattie, to wake up and see her first thing in the morning. It was like a dream come true.

## 26

The sun was shining in a thin line through the barely-open drapes the next morning when Mattie woke up. She was at first confused, not remembering where she was. The bed in Dylan's room was not against the same wall as it was in the room she was occupying. As a result, she felt some confusion when she initially woke up.

It didn't take long for her to grasp where she was and what situation she was in. Grumbling to herself, she slid out of bed and stepped carefully over a snoozing Dylan, who had created a makeshift bed on the floor nearby.

Luke wasn't in the main room when Mattie left Dylan's. She went down the hall on silent feet, opening her door and slipping inside quietly. She let the door softly click behind her before crossing the room to the bed.

The day before, she had laid out a new dress she'd purchased in town. She had no dresses like it and hoped to keep it for a while. Of course, next year, it would be out of fashion, but she'd wear it anyway. She didn't care whether she was keeping up with fashion trends or not. She liked the style. It was pretty and extremely comfortable on her.

Mattie quickly put her clothes on and pulled a brush through her unruly auburn waves. They sprang back to where they had been, but now they were smoothly disheveled. Unhappy with the way it looked, she grabbed a bonnet from the back of her dressed table and pulled it roughly over her head.

She scrubbed her teeth with a towel and inspected herself in the dirty, cracked mirror that was almost too high for her to look into. Only then did she hurry out the door.

Mattie didn't expect the looks the men gave her when Dylan opened the door to see her standing there in her new dress. His eyebrows shot up. She didn't question how he was feeling about the way she was dressed. The look of approval was obvious on his face.

"Was I right?" she demanded, stepping into his

room and twirling around so they could see the entire package.

"You were right," Dylan remarked, closing his door and eyeing her as he finished buttoning his shirt and tucking it into his trousers. "But I didn't say it wasn't going to look good on you, Mattie, so technically, I wasn't wrong either."

They both laughed.

They discussed their plan for the day until he and Luke were ready to leave.

"Are you okay this morning?" Dylan murmured to her as they went down the corridor to the front of the boarding house. She moved her eyes to his face. Her breath was almost taken away by the look she saw there. She couldn't be one hundred percent certain, but she would have sworn what she saw there was love. Pure and simple. No bells or whistles. Just love.

"I, uh, yes, I'm... feeling quite well, thank you. Still nervous, of course. But I am feeling more confident today than I did yesterday. I like our plan. I don't see why it won't work. The bandits don't know we know where they are keeping Franklin and Lauren. It seems so simple to just go in and get them when they leave. Can it really be that easy?"

She saw the look of doubt on his face, even

though he probably thought he was hiding it behind a façade of confidence. Once again, she was overcome with a sense of gratitude that she wasn't doing this alone. That outward appearance of confidence was one of the things that was spurring her on, giving her the bravery and courage to do what needed to be done.

She wouldn't let herself think that it only took one of the bandits forgetting something at their rented house and coming back, catching them in the act. A fight would ensue, probably with guns, which meant she and her siblings were at great risk. They would have to do what they had to do as quickly as possible. Once Lauren and Franklin were back with her, she would feel a lot better about the situation. She didn't care if she had to run all the way back to Bighorn. As long as she had her siblings with her, she would feel whole again.

The first thing the three of them did was go to the restaurant to get something to eat. The second thing they would do was to go to the general store and purchase any supplies they needed before their trip back to Bighorn. Mattie wanted to make sure she had some food for her siblings, who were bound to be starving to death. She didn't trust the bandits to feed them. It had been three days.

The thought that the bandits might not even be feeding her siblings only set fuel to an already blazing fire. She had to rein in her thoughts before they got away from her and prevented her from thinking straight. If there was ever a time to think straight, now was it.

She and Luke stood outside the mercantile, waiting for Dylan, who'd gone in alone. It was their job to keep their eyes open and see if they could catch sight of one of the bandits. Not that they really knew what the two, possibly three, other members of the gang were doing.

The thought that frightened Mattie passed through her mind. What if the bandits just sent one of their men out to take care of errands, such as looking for a response at the Postmaster's. How long would they have to wait for everyone to leave the house? They would have to break in and use their guns if there was never a time for them to go in unnoticed.

Mattie watched Dylan moving about inside the shop.

"He's a good man," Luke said, drawing her attention to him. She nodded.

"I've noticed that," she replied, keeping her voice low.

"Is that so?" He sounded surprised. Mattie wondered why. She drew her eyebrows together and turned halfway toward him, striking a defiant pose.

"Is there a problem with my feelings? You don't want me to notice your partner is a good man? That seems a bit odd, don't you think?"

Luke's eyebrows remained raised as he spoke. His face didn't relax until he'd said his peace.

"It's not odd, and I think he'd be very happy to hear it if I'm completely honest with you. It's just..."

Mattie waited, her eyes directly on the young man's face. He was handsome, but her butterflies weren't for him. They were for Dylan. "Go ahead. Tell me what is on your mind."

"I reckon I'm surprised to hear it because of the way he's acted about women for the past five or so years. Since we were eighteen, I'd say. I know his pa was a good man, too, but he knew when women should keep quiet and when they should speak." He lifted both hands in a surrendering motion and grinned at her. "His words, not mine, I swear. I don't care whether you are washing dishes, making the food, or working all day long at a job for the government."

Mattie couldn't help scoffing. Like she would ever be in government, much less think about it. She didn't want to be noticed and spoken to by hundreds of strangers around the country.

"That's not going to happen," she remarked sarcastically.

He shrugged, continuing his somber look. "You never know. It's the future, right? We're hurtling toward it, aren't we?"

Mattie grunted. "So, you think he's changed his views, huh? You mean about all that chauvinistic stuff about women being in the kitchen, raising babies, and leaving the world to the men?"

"That's what I mean, yes. He's been on about that magazine for a while now. And it appears you've gone and changed his mind. He doesn't want to do the magazine for men anymore."

Mattie was pleased to hear it. "And what is it he wants to change it to?"

Luke laughed. "That's just the thing. He doesn't know. So we will be asking for a loan for the magazine from the bank here before we go. It's a bit amazing when I think about it."

"Oh?" Mattie was surprised.

"Yeah, that's what we came out here for anyway. And now you've gone and changed his mind about women. Now it will be a totally different magazine."

Her eyebrows shot up. "I can't say I'm sorry about

that. But tell me, why didn't he just ask me for a loan?"

"He didn't know you when we made that decision, Mattie. And now he wouldn't ask you because he doesn't know you and you don't know him and a business transaction isn't the best way to start a relationship. Is it?"

She agreed with him, shaking her head. He'd said relationship. Just hearing the word escape from Luke's mouth made her stomach do flip-flops and her heart pound hard in her chest. "No," she replied. "It isn't."

If a relationship was what Dylan wanted, she thought, a relationship he would have.

## 27

Dylan stepped onto the wooden walkway and approached the two standing at the end of the short deck, talking. They both spotted him at the same time and stopped talking abruptly, a dead giveaway that they'd been talking about him.

For some odd reason, he was able to dismiss it. He was sure even if they had been talking about him, it was all good things. He trusted them and knew they were both on his side.

"I've secured the horses we're going to need. Now, all we have to do is go up there and wait." He moved his eyes between the two of them. "I suggest two of us go to the house to get the sibs and one hang back with the horses to bring out at the right time so we can all jump on them and skedaddle out of there."

"I want to go in and free them," Mattie said anxiously. "One of you can stay with the horses."

"It's too dangerous for you to come to the house," Dylan stated. "You stay back with the horses."

"All right, wait a minute," Luke held up both hands and lowered his chin, not looking at either of them. "We aren't going to argue about this." He turned a direct look to Dylan. "You just heard her say she wants to be there for her brother and sister. From the last two days, I'd think you would know that while she'll listen to your suggestions, she's going to do what she wants. If it was your siblings, would you want to wait behind?"

"No, but I'm a man. We don't think the same."

"Oh," Mattie huffed, rolling her eyes and turning sideways so she wasn't facing him. Luke gave him a reproachful look.

"I thought you'd left that way of thinking behind," Luke said, trying to regain the attention. Dylan cast a worried look at Mattie. He hadn't meant that the way it came out. He held up his hand to Luke and shook his head.

"Let me explain. Mattie, please let me explain what I meant."

Mattie raised her eyebrows at him. If that look she was giving him was as affectionate as it looked, he wouldn't have to say much to get her to change her mind. Still, he wanted to tell the truth. He had, in fact, changed his opinions on a great many things when it came to the topic of a woman's role in society.

"The only reason..." She turned her head away from him, letting her eyes wander to the other side of the street. He stopped speaking and waited until she gave him a questioning look. Only then did he continue to speak, "the only reason I said that was because your siblings might be badly hurt. You will be in shock when you see them. And what if they are both unconscious? Can you carry your sister?"

Mattie hesitated, a skeptical look on her face. Dylan nodded. "You see? That's why I asked. I don't need you struggling and falling with her on your shoulders if I can help it. I'm not trying to belittle you. I'm trying to explain why sometimes the last thing you need is another burden when you're already dealing with so much. Luke and I are strong. Stronger than you. We can handle the weight. You will struggle, you know it. Even if you're fine for a little bit, if she's unconscious, that would constitute dead weight. More than you can handle, I'm afraid. You're strong and brave, but you're just not physically strong enough."

"Well, I want to go with you. They won't be expecting you. They won't know who you are."

"Mattie, why are you being difficult?" Dylan said it in the nicest possible way. "You aren't strong enough. Let's not make this more difficult. They already have your siblings. They can just grab you, too, and maybe they'll be so frustrated by all this mess, they'll just decide to kill you all and break their comrades out of jail themselves. Just let us handle this. You'll be able to see from where you are. You'll know what's happening."

"Is that so?" Mattie raised one eyebrow. "You seem very sure. Have you already picked out a spot for me?"

"Yes," Dylan responded immediately, the grounds around the small house the siblings were in coming to his mind's eye. He could see the patch of trees surrounding the fairly large pond nearby. Not only were there trees growing around the pond, there were flowers, plenty of grass, and bushes galore. That meant the pond was virtually hidden from the house. The only reason he knew of it was that he'd spotted it when he explored the house before he even found the door or the outside stairs to the cellar. "I saw it yesterday. Come on. They're waiting for us at the saddle shop now that you mention it. But I thought it best that we wait until we are ready to actually go to the place before we retrieved them. Just in case we're seen by the bandits."

He'd noticed how often both his companions looked around them. It was to make sure there wasn't anyone following them or watching them. So far, they seemed to be going completely unnoticed by anyone, which was exactly what he wanted.

His chest was tight with nervousness, but that wasn't something he was going to admit to the two of them. Especially not Mattie. He wanted to be her rock. The one person she could count on. And he wanted to return the favor in equal measure. They would be partners.

He even surprised himself with all of this.

"It will be noon in a quarter of an hour," Luke said. "I think we should go to the house now. It's the warmest time of the day, and the bandits will want to be out and about by now, getting their supplies for the breakout tonight."

Dylan chuckled at the volume with which Luke

spoke. You'd think he was announcing a big dance for charity work to be held that night. "All right, all right. Don't give us away now," he said, shaking his head at his partner, who grinned. "Let's go get the horses."

## 28

D ylan was pleased with the horses the stable had provided them—for a hefty fee. They were fine beasts and would make it the entire way back to Bighorn with minimal trouble and only a few stops. He was anxious to get back to normal life, anxious for all of this to be over so he could express his true feelings for Mattie and ask her to be his bride.

Two days with a confident, strong woman had been all it took to break his convictions on a woman's place in society. He was even pondering that women might make equal and sometimes better and more contributions to society in many areas.

They rode the horses to the pathway of the house where Franklin and Lauren were being held.

Once there, the three pulled the extra two horses behind them, allowing Dylan to lead them to where they would stay and wait for the two men to bring the kidnapped out. They tied the horses to low-hanging branches near the water. They would have plenty of opportunities to get a drink and graze off some of the grass surrounding the pond.

There were horses in front of the house, indicating the men were still there. As suspected, there were three horses. Including the two in the jail, that was five suspects in the gang.

Dylan peered through the bushes at the front door of the house, wishing it would open and they'd all come filing out. If he had a sniper rifle, he would shoot each of them as they came out. How was he to know which one killed the engineer on the train? It was likely they were all guilty of that most horrific crime at one point or another.

"See any movement yet?" He heard from beside him, making him look over abruptly. Luke only glanced at him before looking at the silent house.

"Not yet," Dylan grumbled. "I'm still worried only one will go. They'd have to be pretty stupid for all of them to go, leaving no one in charge. But I really haven't seen much to impress me about these men. It's like they don't know what they're doing from one minute to the next and are just doing random things, whatever comes to their minds."

"Like they don't have a leader."

Luke's remark set off an alarm bell in Dylan's head. He raised his eyebrows and gave his friend an attentive look. "I think you hit the nail on the head. All I keep thinking is that they aren't well-organized. That's what happens when you don't have anyone in charge and everyone is calling their own shots. Someone probably mentions something, and the rest just go along with it." He shifted his feet underneath where he was crouched, looking through the trees and bushes with narrow eyes, wishing the three bandits would just leave so they could go in and get the siblings out. If they could just do it quickly, the whole thing would be smoothly carried out.

Luke was in a similar position, crouched with his arms propped on his legs, looking through the leaves of the trees toward the house. "I hope they can't see us from there. If you did, surely they can, too."

"Only if they are where I was yesterday. That would be out back. They aren't looking out the dirty windows of the cellar. They wouldn't be able to see much through that grime anyway."

He stopped speaking when the door of the house

opened up. Instinctively, he reached over and grabbed Luke's arm, sucking through his teeth.

"I see them," Luke whispered loudly, his entire body visibly stiffening.

Dylan understood that. His body reacted the same way. He froze where he was, watching the men come out of the house one by one. Dylan heard Mattie approaching from behind them and turned swiftly to gesture frantically at her to get down.

Her eyes opened wide like saucers, and she dropped.

He turned back to the men, watching as they wordlessly went to their horses, mounted, turned the animals toward the main road, and trotted off.

He was a little astonished by how easily that had gone down. If they hadn't found this house, they would have never found the siblings, of that he was certain. He made a mental note to tell Mattie good on her for coming up with the idea of the drag marks. That had been the first and most valuable clue.

"Where do you suppose they are going?" Mattie asked, maintaining a low voice, even though the men on horseback were long gone by then and Dylan and Luke were prepared to go get her siblings.

"Does it matter?" Dylan asked, feeling a sense of urgency pass through him.

"I just hope they are gone for a while."

Dylan shook his head. "No need. Won't take us long to get in there and get them out. I promise. In fact, why are we standing around talking? Come on, Luke. Let's go get them."

"Yes, boss," Luke replied with a flash of a grin. "Let's go get them."

Dylan gave his friend a sarcastic look.

"Be careful, Dylan," Mattie said quietly, gazing up at him in such a way that his body lit up with flames, his thighs tingled, and his heart raced.

"I will," he replied in a low voice. "you know I will."

With one last look down the path to the main road, Dylan hurried across the side yard with Luke right behind him. Both men jumped up the steps and crossed the porch in just a few steps.

The door was, of course, locked. But that didn't deter Luke, who pulled out a small tool he'd designed while at the academy. It had a tiny prying bar on one side, and he used it to unlock the door. Dylan didn't ask how he did it. He was just glad Luke had the knowledge to do it in the first place.

The door swung open, and Luke gave Dylan a look of pride.

Dylan chuckled. "Awful proud of yourself for being an outlaw when ya wanna be."

Luke laughed with him. They moved through the house quickly, looking for a door to lead them to the cellar. When he spotted it, Dylan called out to Luke.

"Over here," he yelled, waving one hand in the air. Luke approached as Dylan yanked the door open. He trundled down the steps, not caring if he made any noise. In fact, he was hoping he was making enough noise to arouse the kidnap victims and make them aware that someone was in the room. It would only be terrifying for them until they found out who he and Luke were. He couldn't fault them that fear. After an ordeal like they'd been put through, they might lash out at him.

He would be prepared.

The light from the dirty windows showed them the way. After their eyes adjusted to the dimness in the cellar, Dylan and Luke were able to see the two siblings.

He went directly to the girl, pulling the sack cloth from over her head. She was staring at him with wide green eyes. For a moment, he feared she was going to spit on him.

"Who are you?" she demanded.

By this time, Luke had gotten Franklin's hood off. He was also conscious. When he saw the two of them, his face lit up, and to his sister's ultimate confusion and surprise, he cried out, "Dylan. Luke. Thank God in Heaven, it's you."

## 29

Mattie stared at the door of the little house for so long her eyes went dry. She blinked rapidly, glancing down the road to make sure the bandits weren't returning. Her heart was doing leaps in her chest every time she thought of them coming back and shooting them all dead right then and there.

She was in the middle of a reverie, picturing what she would do if that actually happened when the door opened again, and Lauren came out first.

Mattie cried out, jumping up and down and clapping her hands together. She had pulled all the horses to the same spot around the pond. She dashed over to them and grabbed all the reins she could in one hand. Without mounting her own horse, she led them out of the oasis-type area to the clearing in front of the house.

"Mattie." It was Franklin who cried out to her, throwing his arms up in the air to give her a kiss.

"Franklin. Oh, Franklin, Lauren, how good to see you and know you're all right. Lauren.... Lauren..." She dropped the reins where they were, not noticing until after the fact that Luke dashed over and took the reins in hand. She ran to her sister, her arms spread out wide. When she got there, Franklin had moved closer to Lauren, so she was able to wrap them around both her beloved sister and brother.

"I can't believe this. How wonderful." She could barely see through the tears in her eyes. They were tears of delighted joy, but they made her vision very blurry. She laughed at her own thoughts and squeezed Franklin and Lauren with everything she had.

"Come on, let's get out of here," Dylan said urgently, his eyes on the road behind them. "I don't want to be here when they come back. Come on."

Mattie, reluctantly letting her siblings go from her grasp, obeyed his suggestion, climbing up into the saddle. She knew how important it was that they leave as quickly as possible.

As they rode away from the little house, Dylan

taking the lead, she eyed her sister, wondering if she would ever get the real truth from her. She pulled her horse up alongside Lauren's, getting her attention. She knew what she was going to ask was something that they were all wondering about. It made her feel a little sick to her stomach to ask, but it was necessary.

"It's really good to see you safe and sound, Lauren," she said, using the gentlest tone she could muster, "but how did you get in that situation? How did they kidnap you? It was from the party, right?"

Lauren's cheeks flushed. She looked hesitant to answer, and when she paused for a prolonged period of time, Lauren couldn't help feeling her sister was devastated by something, something she had likely done.

"If you have something to confess, Lauren," Mattie continued, her voice level dropping even more, "I want you to know I am not going to judge you for what you did. I think you were only doing what you thought was best."

"I wish I could think like you, Mattie. So many people love and respect you. I get a little upset sometimes."

Mattie wondered if her sister was confessing to orchestrating the whole fiasco-turned-nightmare. It would be devastating to think that the only option they didn't want to be true behind this scheme turned out to be right.

"I didn't mean for anything bad to happen," Lauren continued in a sheepish tone, not returning her sister's glances.

Mattie didn't know whether to be furious or feel sorry for the girl.

"Just tell me what you did, Lauren. Get it off your chest, and you'll feel better, I promise."

Lauren hesitated again, and when she spoke, Mattie heard the tears in her voice.

"At the party," she began. "That was when all this started. I... I saw you dancing with that Brian Belhap and..."

Mattie struggled not to let her temper get the better of her. So it all had been Lauren's doing, to begin with. Because she was jealous. Mattie held in her frustration, listening to her sister, trying to sympathize instead of getting angry.

"Goodness, Lauren," she said, shaking her head. "What did you do?"

"I just wanted to get a little attention and make Mama and Papa notice me more," she wailed, breaking down in tears.

"Stay calm, Lauren," Mattie ordered in a big-sister tone. Lauren gulped as she tried to stop her tears. She swiped the back of one hand over the tears angrily.

"I'm trying to stay calm. But I... I know this was all my fault. Everything. After asking Kyle if he wanted to help me out, it was all right at first. I thought things would be fine, and I would stay with them for a couple of days and then show up at home a little dirty but no worse for wear."

"So, what changed?" Mattie noticed the others were also listening with keen ears.

"Kyle's friend, Mallory, came to the place we were staying in at first. Before we came here, you know. That was a shack in Bighorn. I... I didn't expect to be put on a train to God knows where."

She looked like she was going to cry again, so Mattie gave her a hard stare. Lauren nodded and got herself under control.

"Anyways, after Mallory started being there all the time—I think he might have been the leader of the group, at least at one point in time. He started calling the shots. He said it's not just business for him. It's personal."

Mattie frowned deep. "Personal. Maybe that means he's a criminal Papa put in jail. Maybe that's why he's being so reckless. He wants to go back to jail. The undesirables go in there, and that's what he likes."

Lauren was giving her a frightened stare while Franklin's eyes were intelligently agreed. She even caught the slight nod of her head.

Through her stare, a spark of light came to Lauren's eyes. Mattie saw it and leaned in. "That means... that means he was going to kill us. He never intended to let us go. He was going to kill us."

Mattie heard the fear returning to her sister's voice.

"You have to stay calm, Lauren. Take deep breaths and hold them for a few seconds before letting them out slowly. It will help your heart rate go down. I can see how upset you are. It's going to be okay now. Now everything will be fine. It will go back to normal. We're going home, aren't we?"

"But what's going to happen to those men? Where will they be taken? Will they even be arrested?"

"We know they kidnapped *you*," Mattie replied. "That's all the evidence we need. Just showing up with you. And with Franklin. They got him, too. But it's Dylan and Luke who will speak to the sheriff about it. They will go and arrest these vermin. And we'll never be bothered by them again."

"Good," Lauren exclaimed as if nothing could change the outcome they wanted. "I don't ever want to see Kyle or any of them ever again. Never."

"You won't. They might have to stand in front of Papa, but they won't be able to touch you Ever again."

They rode quietly until they got to the border of Trumperton, where Dylan stopped them, putting one fist up in the air.

"We're going to let you three go on from here alone. Mattie, you've got the map I bought for you?"

"I have it," Mattie replied, whipping the folded map from her back pocket. She held it up and shook it.

"Wonderful. I took the liberty of tracing the path home with a dark pen, in case you need any help."

As Mattie said thank you, and they all said their goodbyes for now, Mattie examined the face of the man she wanted to spend the rest of her life with. Once a chauvinist, Dylan Sullivan had turned out to be much deeper, an intelligent and highly compassionate man.

She would almost agree to change her views on her own rights and freedoms just so she could say she agreed with him.

Almost.

## 30

The jailhouse was almost what one might call quiet when the two men entered. The sheriff was standing in front of a table where a few items had been scattered. He glanced up when Luke and Dylan walked in.

"Well, hello there," he said. "You lookin' for stolen property? For some reason, a few of these things were all collected by the bandits but not claimed by the owners."

Sheriff Dawson—as was indicated by the name tag over his badge—turned to grin at them. I don't suppose this fancy mirror belongs to either of you?"

Dylan shook his head. "No, sir."

"Strange," the sheriff mumbled, his eyes

returning to the few remaining items from the bandit's loot. "Who would refuse to claim their items? Never heard anything like it."

"We came to tell you there are three more bandits on the loose," Dylan said in a hurry. "They are planning a breakout tonight. You might want to warn your men. If you would rather, my business partner and I would be glad to show you where the house is that they rented. You will find the two chairs in the cellar where they had two victims they'd kidnapped and were holding."

Sheriff Dawson froze at the beginning of Dylan's speech and was still staring at him by the end of it.

"And you know this how?"

"We've been on the run with... with our eyes open for any strange activity. We're... kind of like... bounty hunters in a sense. We got wind that they were being held—the Holbrook son and one of their daughters—and thought it would be profitable to find them for the Judge and his wife."

"Judge Holbrook's kids?" the sheriff asked, his eyes turning sharp.

Dylan wondered if the two men knew each other. That would certainly explain that odd reaction. "Yes, sir, that's right."

"Well, there's a reward for them kids," the sheriff continued in an incredulous voice. "You'll be gettin' that, at least. Where are they now? The Holbrook kids?"

"They are on their way back to Bighorn, Texas. That's their home."

"Good work, young man. And you, too." As he spoke, he reached over and took Dylan's hand, pumping it vigorously. When he let go, he captured Luke's. Dylan couldn't help laughing inside. Luke wasn't happy about the man touching him, but he was tolerant and put up with it.

"Are we going to get those men? They came in town for supplies, and now is probably the best time to catch them unawares, don't you think?"

The sheriff didn't hesitate to nod. "Yes. You are right. However, you might want to leave this up to the professionals, eh?"

"We have to show you where the house is," Dylan replied logically.

"Ah. Yes, of course. All right, let me get a couple of deputies, and we'll go. This should make for an interesting read in the newspaper."

Dylan was only a little confused by the callous nature the sheriff had about arresting three more men who had committed the crime of kidnapping and robbery.

Ten minutes later, the two men were leading the sheriff and three deputies to the house in the woods. Seeing the horses in front of the house made Dylan's stomach turn with nervousness.

"Stop," the sheriff said. This time, Dylan heard deadly seriousness in the man's voice. "Everyone stop."

The men turned their horses at an angle, so they were facing inside an awkward oval.

"We're going in quiet," the sheriff said. "We don't want to spook these men and create a firestorm of bullets flying through the air, do we?"

Dylan wondered if he really heard amusement in the man's voice or if it was all his imagination. The sheriff pointed to two of his deputies. "You two go around back. Make sure these men don't get out that way. We'll go in the front."

"How are you going to do that?" Dylan asked curiously.

"Gonna knock on the darned door, that's what I'm gonna do," the sheriff responded, not looking at Dylan. As if to prove a point, he dismounted just outside the six steps that led up to the porch. He ascended the steps and casually strolled to the front door. He knocked, placing his hands on his belt as if he had to hold up his pants.

It felt to Dylan like everyone was holding their breath. He knew he was holding his, staring at the door, anticipating its opening.

When it did, it was immediately slammed again, right in the sheriff's face.

"Hey," the sheriff called out, sounding surprised. "Open the door. You in there. Open this door." He banged hard on the door, calling out.

Dylan heard sounds coming from the back of the house. The sheriff ran to the edge of the porch and leaped to the ground, completely missing all the steps.

"They're tryin' ta get away," he yelled to the deputies who had stayed around front. "Come on, boys. Let's go round us some kidnappers."

Dylan held out his hand when he saw Luke's horse moving forward. He looked over at his friend. "This isn't our fight," he said. "Let's go to the train station and get on that train before it leaves."

Luke looked surprised, moving his eyes to the small house and back to his friend. "You don't want to be here when they are apprehended?"

Dylan shook his head, turning his horse to go away from the commotion and violence. "Naw. What do they need us for? We don't have badges. I want to get to the train station so I can ride back on the same train as Mattie."

"You gonna marry that girl?" Luke teased, grinning wide.

"No need to tease," Dylan responded in a smooth voice. "I am gonna marry her. Come hell or high water. I'm gonna marry her."

He felt good saying that. He couldn't wait to say it to Mattie. He wasn't even worried that she would say no. No woman in the world could look at a man the way she looked at him and say no to marriage. He was anxious to spend the rest of his life with the woman who had changed his life forever.

They rode most of the way to the train station quietly, talking randomly but mostly staying to themselves. Dylan had his own thoughts to ponder. He planned to send a letter to Sheriff Dawson of Trumperton, telling him exactly what had happened. He would leave the address for them to get in touch with him but not the Holbrooks. They were a public figure family, and he was not obliged to give out their personal information to anyone.

The train station loomed in the distance, the long tracks weaving through the town, though the building that served as a ticket office was minute compared to the platform that stretched out in front of it. It was as though the good townsfolk of Trumperton had a feeling they were going to get a whole lot of visitors at one time someday.

His heart jumped into overdrive when Dylan heard the whistle of the train as it got started and prepared to leave the station.

"Hurry," he exclaimed, jabbing his heels into his horse's flanks to get him to gallop. "Let's go. Hurry, Luke. Hurry."

"I'm right behind you, Dylan," he heard as they both sped up their horses.

He hopped off his horse as soon as he got to the platform. He bolted up the short three steps to the walkway and began to run. The train was moving now. It wasn't moving very fast, but it was definitely moving.

He heard the cry of the train attendant. "All aboard."

He heard the slapping of the wheels as they began to rotate on the tracks.

"Don't," he said into the loud noise of the train moving into motion. "Don't leave without me. Don't leave without me."

Smoke filled the air around him, making it hard

to see and even harder to breathe. He waved his hand in front of his face.

He didn't even think about where Luke was. All he wanted to do was find the car with his future bride in it.

# EPILOGUE

**M**attie stared out the window. She'd been hoping Dylan—and Luke, too, of course—would make it to the train station on time. All they'd had to do was take the sheriff and a few deputies to the house the bandits had been using. She refused to think the men might have been caught up in some gun battle or something. She found herself wishing she had stayed with them—or at least gone back to the house with them.

The train began to move. Smoke billowed from overhead, obscuring much of Mattie's view through the glass. It was okay, though. She didn't really have anything to see.

Not a moment passed after she thought those words when she saw Dylan burst through a thick cloud of smoke, his eyes frantically searching the windows.

Was he looking for her? Of course, he was. Who else would he be searching for?

She clapped her hands together and shot to her feet, staring at him through the window. She could feel the train moving faster and faster, just like her heart.

Mattie pressed her hands flat against the glass, willing it to get out of her way so she could reach out, grab him, and pull him in.

Since there was no way to do that from where she was, she ran out of the cabin she'd been occupying and fled to the nearest outside door. She yanked it open, despite the written instructions next to it, saying it should not be opened with the train was in motion.

She wondered if he'd seen her.

She managed to get the door open fairly easily, and the answer to her question was standing right in front of her. Dylan had seen her. He probably saw her racing toward the door to open it for him. Seconds later, he was leaping up the steps into the cabin, and Luke was right behind him.

"Dylan," she cried out. "You made it."

"Of course I made it," he stated as if nothing bad could ever have happened to him. "I will always come for you, no matter where you are or what's happened to you. I will always come for you."

"Haven't I told you two before not to show such love and emotion in front of a single, lonely man like me?" Luke quipped, eyeing the two of them through narrowed lids. He pushed past them. "Where's the family?"

Mattie grinned at the tall blond man, affection for his humor and friendship filling her chest. "That way," she said, pointing. "Third on the left. Yes, right there."

Luke nodded at her when he got to the door, slid it open, and disappeared on the other side.

"I reckon we could go to the dining car and enjoy a nice cocktail or a cup of tea." Dylan offered, his voice warm. She felt a tingle slide through her and nodded vigorously.

"I'd like that a lot," she said. "I think we have a lot to talk about."

He raised his eyebrows, slowly taking her hand, sending a sensation straight through her arm directly to her heart. Cupid's arrow? She thought maybe so. She couldn't even be embarrassed that she had stars in her eyes for him.

"We do?"

"Yes, we do." She wondered if he knew what she was referring to and gazed at him lovingly, trying to figure it out. The twitching of his lips gave her the indication he was teasing her. It made her feel giddy inside to know he was playing with her. She thought it was the cutest thing when a man played that way.

They began walking, side by side when they could, single file when someone needed to pass them by.

"Exactly what is it we need to talk about?" Dylan asked.

"I think you know what," she responded in a lighthearted tone. "We are in love. Aren't we." She didn't make her last words a question. She knew for a fact that he was in love with her.

"We've only known each other for about three days," Dylan responded. "Are you sure about that?"

Mattie tried not to take that as a real question. Maybe he was just being cautious. Maybe, for some reason, only God knew, he thought she was just his friend.

Instead of trying to explain herself, Mattie stopped in the middle of the train corridor and pulled him to her. She lifted up on her tiptoes and pressed her lips against his. The kiss was, she thought, a little awkward at first, but she knew she'd caught Dylan completely off guard.

The kiss quickly evolved into something much, much deeper. His lips against hers lit her body on fire. Her knees became weak and wobbly. She had to wrap her arms around his neck to hold herself up on weakened feet. She didn't need to hold on, though, not really.

His strong arms had wrapped around her waist, and he was holding her against him so tightly she could barely breathe. She thought for a moment she really might suffocate if they didn't take a break.

But she didn't want to stop the kiss. She wanted it to last forever. The passion that flowed through her from him made her sure she was making the right decision.

When they finally pulled away from each other, Dylan lowered his head and pressed it against her forehead. He closed his eyes and whispered the words Mattie wanted to hear, the words she never thought she would hear, especially not from someone who had once believed women were second-class citizens unable to make rational decisions.

"Mattie, will you marry me?"

She felt the blood rush from her head to her toes. Her stomach exploded with butterflies. She responded breathlessly, the only way she could speak at a time like that.

"Yes, Dylan. I will marry you. Oh yes, I will."

Click here for more Blythe Carver books!

Sign up for the newsletter to be notified of new releases.

Click on link for
Newsletter
or put this in your browser window:

landing.mailerlite.com/webforms/landing/p6l2s1

CPSIA information can be obtained
at www.ICGtesting.com
Printed in the USA
LVHW041946090723
751958LV00003B/358